THE
RED KITE

THE
RED KITE

by
Ian Carter

ARLEQUIN PRESS

ISBN 10 1-905268-03-3

ISBN 13 978-1-905268-03-0

First published 2001
Second Edition 2007

ARLEQUIN PRESS
A Division of CJ Wildbird Foods Ltd
The Rea, Upton Magna, Shrewsbury SY4 4UR

Text: © Ian Carter
Maps: © Arlequin Press
Illustrations: © Dan Powell
Photographs: © the individual photographers as credited

A catalogue record for this book is available.

Dedication

For Alice and Benedict

Adult Red Kite and small chicks at the nest   *(Carlos Sanchez Alonso)*

ACKNOWLEDGEMENTS

My involvement with the Red Kite began, in 1995, with the start of the central England reintroduction project and I would firstly like to thank those individuals who made this work possible. Jose Lara Zabia and Maria Teressa Tarazona provided invaluable help in arranging for nestlings to be collected from central Spain, and permission to take birds was granted by the Junta de Castilla y León (Dirección General del Medio Natural). Many individuals were involved in collecting nestlings from Spain and I would like, in particular, to thank Ian Evans, Phil Grice, Rod Hall MBE, Karl Ivens, Charlie Rugeroni, Peter Stevens, Robert Thomas and Jonathan Wray. In addition, the Southern England Kite Group, including Mick McQuaid, Nigel Snell and Peter Stevens, helped with the translocation of Red Kites within England, and Tony Cross and Nick Fox provided rescued young from Wales.

I shared the task of monitoring released birds and studying the subsequently re-established population in central England with John Cornell, Derek Holman, Karl Ivens (Forest Enterprise), Momo Medina and Deborah Ottway. Robert Thomas was a frequent companion in the field and endured many bone-chilling winter afternoons at the main communal roost in order to help gather information on wing-tagged birds. Sean Walls, Andrew Roy and Brian Cresswell at Biotrack Ltd provided invaluable advice on the fitting of radio-transmitters to released birds.

I have learnt a great deal over the past twelve years through conversations with others involved with Red Kite conservation, including members of the Red Kite Coordination Group which oversees Red Kite conservation work in the United Kingdom. Colin Crooke, Tony Cross, Alistair Crowle, Peter Davis, Will Dixon, Andy Douse, Kevin Duffy, Brian Etheridge, Robert Kenward, Mick McQuaid, Dionysios Ntampakis, Duncan Orr-Ewing, Lorcan O'Toole, Tim Page, David Parkin, Jemima Parry-Jones, Cathy Rose, Doug Simpson, Nigel Snell, Peter Stevens, Peter Walters Davies, Sian Whitehead and Javier Viñuela have all helped to further our understanding of the Red Kite and the measures required to improve its fortunes in Britain and elsewhere. The late Roger Clarke's expertise was invaluable during studies of diet and, as author of *Montagu's Harrier*, it was he who first suggested that the Red Kite would make a useful addition to this series of monographs.

Information on the main mortality factors currently affecting Red Kites in England has been built up as a result of post-mortems carried out by Andrew Cunningham, Tracey Howard, James Kirkwood, Iain McGill, Tony Sainsbury and Sue Thornton at the Zoological Society of London's, Institute of Zoology.

Pesticide residues in Red Kite tissues were determined by analysis at the Central Science Laboratory (CSL) and the Centre for Ecology and Hydrology (CEH), and Mark Fletcher (CSL), Richard Shore (CEH), Alastair Burn, Peter Karner and Paul Butt (Natural England) have provided much guidance on this subject.

The following staff at RSPB (in addition to some of the individuals named above) have been directly involved with work on the Red Kite in England and are thanked for their help: Katherine Davies, Graham Elliot, Richard Gregory, Steve Holliday, Julian Hughes, Duncan McNiven, Peter Newbery, Guy Shorrock and Simon Wotton.

Andy Brown and Phil Grice at Natural England provided several useful historical references, unearthed during work on their book *Birds in England*. Chris Monk helped to set up a database of records from studies of radio-tagged and wing-tagged birds in central England, from which much information on survival rates, dispersal, home range and habitat-use has been derived. He also helped to collate information on the Red Kite's breeding status in Europe. David Conlin and Selena Carter translated several recent German publications into English, making accessible some very useful accounts of the species in its central European stronghold. Andy Brown, Brian and Margaret Carter, Tony Cross, Brian Etheridge, Mike Gaydon, Phil Grice, Peter Newbery, Doug Simpson and Javier Viñuela made many invaluable comments on the first edition. Steve Dudley edited the revised draft for the second edition and made numerous helpful suggestions and amendments which greatly improved the final result.

CONTENTS

List of Tables

List of Figures

List of Plates

INTRODUCTION

The Red Kite is one of only a handful of birds that manages to thrill and delight almost everyone that is lucky enough to see it at close quarters. It has all the attributes required for attracting attention and admiration, including a spectacular plumage, a wonderfully graceful and effortless flight, and the habit of drifting slowly, low over the countryside, where it can be appreciated to full effect. It is, quite simply, one of the world's most impressive birds of prey.

In the time that I have been involved with the Red Kite, I have been repeatedly amazed by the bird's appeal, even to people who have only a casual interest in wildlife. In the reintroduction areas in England and Scotland the Red Kite has become a frequent topic of conversation, and anything up to 200 people have packed into tiny village halls in order to learn more about this new addition to their local countryside. Farmers, gamekeepers and others who spend long hours working outdoors are often particularly enthusiastic as they have more opportunity than most to become familiar with the bird.

The Red Kite is a highly adaptable, generalist species, able to thrive in a wide range of different landscapes provided that the basic requirements of woodland for nesting and roosting, and open areas for foraging, are met. The species has one of the most varied diets of any European bird of prey and will scavenge on almost anything, from the smallest of birds and mammals to the largest of our domestic animals, as well as taking live prey in the form of small mammals, birds and invertebrates. In times gone by, even urban areas provided a home, and the species was one of the first to be given legal protection in Britain for its valuable role in helping to keep the streets clean.

Despite its lack of specialist habitat requirements, the Red Kite has a rather patchy distribution across Europe, and is absent from some areas where the landscape appears to be perfectly suitable. This is mainly a reflection of the bird's extreme vulnerability to human persecution. It is relatively fearless of man, at least in comparison to many other raptors, and so is a regular victim of shooting and, as a scavenger, it often falls victim to illegal poison baits placed out in the open countryside. In areas where levels of persecution are low, the Red Kite is able to thrive and populations have increased dramatically in some countries during the last ten years or so. But where persecution is still common practice, the Red Kite is either absent completely or its numbers are in worrying decline.

The story of the Red Kite in Britain emphasises the degree to which the bird's fortunes have changed at the hands of humans. From being one of our most widespread and familiar birds of prey a few hundred years ago, it came to within a hair's breadth of extinction in the early 1900s, as, along with other birds of prey, it was seen as a threat to gamebirds and livestock. A few pairs found a last refuge in the remote uplands of central Wales, where persecution was less intense, but where the damp, cool climate and unproductive landscape made recovery a painfully slow process. Thankfully, we live in times when attitudes towards birds of prey in Britain, at least amongst a majority of people, have changed for the better. The lack of fear of humans that once hastened the Red Kite's decline is now an asset, allowing it to exploit food sources close to human settlements and providing people with spectacular views. In parts of Britain the Red Kite has, once again, become a regular visitor to rural villages and the edges of small towns and it will even come down to food put out for it in village gardens. A photograph of one bird in the process of snatching up the leftovers from someone's Sunday lunch appeared recently in the national press, and in the accompanying interview, the householder expressed his delight at being able to watch such a magnificent bird from the comfort of his own living room.

One of the most fascinating aspects of the Red Kite is its highly social behaviour in winter. Groups of anything up to several hundred birds gather together at traditional roosts in the late afternoon, often indulging in spectacular communal display-flights above the roost wood, before settling in the trees for the night. At times, the birds seem to be simply enjoying themselves and it is a highly uplifting experience to watch a pre-roost gathering of birds wheeling around in tight formation, with some breaking away from the main group to indulge in rapid, zig-zagging chases. Despite the apparent frivolity of this activity, there are good biological reasons for communal roosting, as well as the pre-roost display-flights, and these are explored in the chapter on social behaviour.

A huge amount of time and resources have been put into efforts to conserve the Red Kite in Britain, both in central Wales, where the once tiny population has now made a substantial recovery, and in England and Scotland where the bird has been reintroduced. The fact that Government-funded bodies, conservation charities and, in some cases, private companies, have been willing to fund this work demonstrates the importance we now place on restoring native species, lost as a result of our own actions in the past. Similar projects have been undertaken with many other birds of prey across Europe and North America, further highlighting both the vulnerability of this group of birds, sitting at the top of the food chain, and the high value placed on their presence in the countryside.

Perhaps the most famous example of a bird restoration project is the ongoing effort in the western United States to save the spectacular California Condor from extinction. A conservation programme has now been running for over 20 years, involving research into the reasons for decline, captive-rearing, and reintroductions at several different sites. A very rough estimate of costs suggests an annual figure in excess of $1 million and there is still a long way to go before the work can be regarded as successful in ensuring the survival of the species.

Although the cost of the Red Kite reintroduction programme falls well short of the amount spent on the California Condor, it nevertheless attracts criticism from some who think that too much money is spent on a minority of high profile species, at the expense of other, more pressing, conservation priorities. It is therefore worth emphasising that well-planned reintroduction projects are not simply about restoring a single species. They can be used to try to promote more wildlife-friendly forms of landscape management and to tackle problems that affect a whole range of different species. The Red Kite reintroduction programme has helped to show that illegal poison baits still threaten birds of prey in Britain and has highlighted problems with accidental secondary poisoning when highly-toxic anticoagulant poisons are used to control rodents. The Red Kite has proved to be a very useful 'flagship' species in trying to tackle these problems and this will benefit a wide range of other species, including, for example, the Buzzard and Barn Owl, also affected by the same problems.

INTRODUCTION TO THE REVISED EDITION

In the six years since the first edition of this book was published, the Red Kite has continued its recovery in Britain. The Welsh population now exceeds 500 pairs and birds have, at long last, spread over the border into western England. The reintroduction programme has continued apace and, as well as a population of over 300 pairs in the Chilterns, birds have now been released at seven other sites in England and Scotland. Building on this success, plans are now well-advanced for releases in Ireland, both north and south of the border, using young birds taken from nests in Wales. Despite the Red Kite's highly social nature and tendency to breed close to others of its own kind, there have been very welcome reports of breeding in areas well away from the release sites in recent years. If this trend continues, the rate at which the Red Kite is able to recolonise Britain will be increased dramatically.

It is not anticipated that the Red Kite will become a common bird in large urban areas, as was the case in medieval times. Nevertheless, the first successful breeding as a result of the 'Northern Kites' reintroduction project involved a pair that reared young 600m away from the edge of urban Gateshead, just 8km away from Newcastle city centre. There have also been sporadic sightings over central London and birds are regularly seen over the centres of Reading and Oxford on the edge of the Chilterns, providing a truly awe-inspiring sight for city dwellers and visitors alike.

The popularity of the Red Kite continues to amaze. In areas where it has become re-established, the bird's name has been adopted by a wide variety of local businesses and its image used in the logos of everything from local schools to village football teams. It has even been incorporated into the official crest of an RAF Squadron based at Benson in the Chilterns. There is now 'Red Kite' beer and, for those seeking a more healthy alternative, 'Red Kite' milk. Public viewing facilities have been set up at a number of sites in England, Wales and Scotland. People now flock to watch Red Kites being fed in front of specially built hides and can even log on to the internet to follow the minute by minute progress of breeding pairs with webcams set up at the nest.

Not all the news is good, however. Although work has continued to try to reduce the threat from poisoning, illegal persecution remains a serious problem, particularly in parts of Scotland. It is revealing to compare the fortunes of the Red Kite populations on the Black Isle in northern Scotland and in the Chilterns of southern England, bearing in mind that releases in these areas started at the same time and involved exactly the same number of birds. In 2006, the Black Isle population stood at 40 pairs, having barely increased in the last five years.

In contrast, the Chilterns population has increased rapidly and is now thought to exceed 300 pairs. Monitoring work by fieldworkers has confirmed that the difference is due almost entirely to the higher number of birds from the Black Isle that are killed by illegal poison baits, the birds being especially vulnerable when they wander onto moorland managed intensively for grouse shooting. On the continent too, the Red Kite's fortunes have varied strongly in recent years with continuing dramatic recoveries in some countries but worrying declines, largely due to human persecution, in others. Much clearly remains to be done before the Red Kite can be regarded as fully secure in Europe. In the Cape Verde Islands the situation is truly depressing. Recent genetic work has gone some way to resolving the mystery of the 'Cape Verde Kite' just as the population appears to have become extinct in the wild.

A noticeable development in the conservation world over recent years is the increasing use of reintroduction projects in order to restore species lost through human actions in the past. When the first edition of this book was published in 2001, the Red Kite was one of only three birds to be have been reintroduced for conservation reasons in Britain, the other two being White-tailed Eagle and Osprey. The ensuing six years have seen projects implemented for Corncrake, Great Bustard and Cirl Bunting in England, and a project involving the Golden Eagle in the Republic of Ireland. There are also plans to set up new release sites for White-tailed Eagles in England, Scotland and Ireland. The huge success of the Red Kite reintroduction programme has undoubtedly played a part in encouraging these new projects.

Ian Carter
October 2007, Norfolk

Chapter 1

DESCRIPTION AND TAXONOMY

Most people who have had the opportunity to watch Red Kites at close quarters will agree that, quite simply, this is one of our most beautiful and spectacular birds of prey. The plumage is a rich mixture of rufous, brown and black, with contrasting large white 'windows' on the underwings, and a long, deeply forked, reddish-brown tail. It is in flight that the bird's full beauty is revealed and its habit of floating slowly, low over open country, together with a relative lack of fear of humans, means that the plumage is often shown off to full effect. With many birds of prey the most frequent views are of a small dot circling high in the sky or a shape, barely registered, as it flashes past at high speed. The Red Kite often allows a more prolonged and considered appraisal, and, with its impressive five-foot wingspan and varied colours, rarely disappoints the observer.

The Red Kite's distinctive cruciform shape, with long, angled wings and long tail, together with its buoyant, effortless flight, make it an easy bird to recognise, even at considerable distance, particularly in Britain where the similar Black Kite is only a rare visitor. When there is little wind and no thermals to exploit, the flight can be more laboured with slow, heavy wing beats and it can then be mistaken for a heron or even a large gull when silhouetted at distance. When perched, much of the contrast between different coloured areas of plumage is lost and the bird appears a rather uniform reddish-brown colour, with only the pale head, and yellow eye and bill, standing out.

Plumage

Full descriptions of plumage can be found in many excellent field guides and handbooks (e.g. Jonsson 1992, Svensson et al. 1999, Forsman 1999) and are therefore not repeated in detail here. A fair appreciation of the bird may be gained from the photographs (see for example Plates 1, 2 & 4) but they do not do full justice to a bird that derives so much of its appeal from the gracefulness and agility of its flight. As with all birds, there is no substitute for direct observation in the field.

The only species with which the Red Kite is likely to be confused is its smaller close relative the Black Kite. This species is common in summer throughout much of the Red Kite's continental range. Given good views, the Red Kite's longer, more deeply forked, reddish tail and reddish-brown plumage on the body and wing coverts are distinctive. The Black Kite (see Plate 3) usually has a much darker plumage with comparatively shorter wings and a less deeply forked tail. With practice, the distinctive colours and shapes of the two species can be picked out, even at considerable distance. The main confusion species for the rare Black Kite in Britain is actually the Marsh Harrier, particularly with an out of context, high-flying, bird where the distinctive V-shape made by the harrier's wings is difficult to discern. The risk of confusion between the two kites is greater with the occasional rufous variant of Black Kite and with the eastern *lineatus* race of Black Kite, although both are very rare across the majority of the Red Kite's European range (Corso 2002, Forsman 2003).

Juvenile Red Kites are more compact than the adults, with slightly shorter wings and a shorter, less deeply forked, tail. This is most apparent in late summer when the young have only recently left the nest and the tail feathers are still growing. At this age, there is a higher risk of confusion with other birds of prey, particularly Black Kites. Close scrutiny may be required to reveal the pale reddish upper-tail and reddish tinge to the body and wing coverts in order to confirm the identification.

7

Juveniles remain separable from adults until their first moult is complete in the following autumn. As well as their paler, more washed out appearance and the differences in shape already described, there are a number of other features worth looking for when trying to age a Red Kite. In late summer and early autumn, when juveniles are in fresh plumage, older birds will be moulting and many will have a rather tatty appearance with missing feathers and noticeable gaps in the wings or tail. The plumage of juveniles, by contrast, is usually immaculate with rarely a feather out of place, giving them a pristine appearance. In flight, the pale fringes to the wing-coverts form a pale line across both the underwing and upperwing of juveniles, and this can be visible at a considerable distance in good light. On a perched juvenile the pale line formed by the upperwing covert fringes is visible on the folded wing, and the darker eye and paler markings on the underbody should also be apparent at close range (see plate 4). These features are most clearly seen in the autumn and early part of the winter.

In late summer, given close views, three age classes are readily separable – recently fledged young (as described above), young fledged in the previous year and adult birds at least two years old. Young from the previous year and adults are both in moult at this time of year but the younger birds still show signs of their immaturity until the moult nears completion in the autumn. The pale tips on the older, unmoulted wing-coverts remain (although they may be reduced as a result of wear), the underbody is still rather pale in comparison to the richer and more heavily streaked appearance of the adults, and the older, unmoulted, tail feathers are clearly paler than those that have already been replaced.

The plumage of Red Kites is generally very consistent and there is certainly not the wide degree of variation between individuals that is shown by the Common Buzzard for example. It is usually only possible to recognise an individual Red Kite if a wing or tail feather is damaged or missing, or, for a short time, by a distinctive pattern of gaps in the wings or tail during the annual moult. A very low proportion of birds, however, appear noticeably paler than normal, with a 'washed-out' appearance due to a lack of the usual dark pigmentation in the feathers. Such birds are known as leucistic rather than true albinos, as some of the dark pigmentation remains and the beak and feet are yellow as in normal birds. They appear to get paler with age and may look almost pure white at a distance. Several of these 'white' birds have occurred in Wales in recent years and, in some cases, have managed to survive for several years (Cross & Davis 2005). It is possible that these 'white' birds suffer from an associated genetic problem which makes them infertile as there have been no confirmed records of successful breeding. In 2005, a Welsh male of this plumage form was found paired to a normal-coloured female but although it is thought that eggs were laid, no chicks were seen and the breeding attempt failed. In Germany, Hille (1995a) was able to recognise individual pale-plumaged birds that returned to the same breeding site for up to four consecutive years.

Moult

Red Kites renew their flight and tail feathers in a single, protracted, moult during the summer. Non-breeding birds, particularly juveniles, usually begin earlier than breeding adults and the distinctive gaps in the wings, as the first feathers are dropped, can be seen from late March onwards.

Breeding adults do not usually start to moult until the incubation phase of the breeding cycle in April or May and it is often the female that begins first. She spends almost all of her time sitting on the nest during the four weeks of incubation and the first 2-3 weeks after the eggs have hatched, and this provides an ideal opportunity to replace as many of the flight feathers as possible. During this period the female often has very noticeable gaps in the wings while the male has only small gaps or is still full-winged. However, this difference between the sexes is not entirely consistent as, in some cases, the male has gaps in the wings early in the season whilst the female remains full-winged well into incubation. Differences in moult pattern can be a very useful method for distinguishing between the two members of a breeding pair at a distance, particularly if marks such as colour rings or wing-tags can be used to confirm the identity of each individual when seen at close range.

During the summer Red Kites are frequently seen with obvious gaps at the same point in each wing due to the loss of moulted feathers

Moulted feathers are often found close to breeding sites. This series from a nest site in central England includes two tail feathers (with a rufous wash), one of the long, mainly black, outer primaries, and a shorter and paler inner primary *(Ian Carter)*

Moult progresses from the innermost primary (the first feather to be lost) towards the tip of the wing in a regular pattern, with the outermost primary last in the sequence. The pattern of moult of the secondaries is less predictable and some, particularly non-breeding, birds can have several gaps in the wings when moult is well advanced. The moult of the twelve tail feathers begins with the two central feathers and appears to progress, in sequence, from the centre to the edge of the tail. By September, the two outer tail feathers, falling short of the tip of the tail, may be the only sign that the moult is not yet complete. In migratory populations in central and northern Europe, moult is not usually completed by the time of the autumn migration and the last feathers are replaced in the winter quarters (Forsman 1999).

It is probable that Red Kites are able to suspend moult during the breeding season, as is known to occur in other raptor species. Individually-marked birds with obvious gaps in the wings early in the breeding season are sometimes full-winged only a few weeks later, well before the time by which the moult could have been completed. It may be advantageous to suspend, or slow, the rate of moult at a stage in the breeding cycle when more active flight is required, such as during the chick rearing period, particularly if food is in short supply. Missing feathers reduce foraging efficiency and could therefore reduce the amount of food that the adults are able to bring to the nestlings. Moult appears to proceed more rapidly towards the end of the breeding season when the duties of rearing young are at an end.

In late summer it is not unusual to drive through an area with a high density of Red Kites and yet see very little evidence of activity. This is, in part, related to moult. Many of the adult birds are moulting heavily at this time and with gaps in the wings and tail, flight becomes more onerous. As a result, they tend to spend less time in the air and more time perched up in trees where they are often difficult to pick out against a backdrop of leaves. Recently fledged young will not be moulting at this time of year but food is at its most plentiful in late summer and they too often spend long periods perched up in trees having no need to make extensive foraging flights.

As with many large birds of prey, not all the flight feathers are always replaced during the annual moult. Red Kites in their second winter, after the completion of their first full moult, sometimes retain several juvenile secondaries and one or more of the outermost juvenile primaries. These feathers appear faded and

This bird, found dead in its second winter, has retained five of its juvenile secondaries. These are visible as groups of two and three feathers that are faded brown, with worn tips, and slightly shorter than the adjacent adult feathers (Ian Carter)

11

are browner than the new feathers although this is extremely difficult to detect on a free-flying bird.

The body feathers and wing-coverts are also replaced during the summer moult, except for a proportion of juveniles that replace some of these feathers during their first winter. Some individuals begin as early as September/October of their first year while others are still in full juvenile plumage in April of their second year (Forsman 1999).

Voice

For much of the year the Red Kite is largely silent and calling is only occasionally heard during squabbles over food, or at communal pre-roost gatherings. As the breeding season approaches it becomes rather more vociferous, particularly close to the nest site. Paired birds call to each other as part of the courtship ritual and calling is frequently heard when there is human disturbance near to an active nest.

Bird calls and songs are extremely difficult to represent accurately in words and there is no substitute for learning sounds through hearing them in the field. The Red Kite's usual call is perhaps closest to that of a Buzzard but is higher in pitch and often with two or three shorter and rapidly repeated, slurred notes after the initial call. Svensson *et al.* (1999) describe it as 'weee-ooh, ee oo, ee oo, ee oo' but there is much variation. In some situations the call is weak and wavering, almost hesitant, but, when a nest site is disturbed, calls can be loud and shrill, and repeated rapidly with real purpose. Somewhat unexpectedly, a brief snatch of song from a Blackbird, Song Thrush or Robin can, initially, be mistaken for the distant call of a Red Kite.

A further source of potential confusion results from the fact that some common woodland birds regularly incorporate mimicry into their songs. We are all familiar with the surprisingly lifelike renditions of car alarms that Starlings, Blackbirds and Song Thrushes sometimes include within their songs. The simple but distinctive call of the Red Kite may be copied in the same way. This has, on occasion, led to considerable frustration for fieldworkers attempting to locate a Red Kite breeding site by following up the calls of what turns out to be the wrong species of bird!

Differences between the sexes

In some birds of prey there is a noticeable size difference between the sexes with females tending to be larger and heavier than males. This is termed 'reversed size dimorphism' as, in most groups of bird where there is a difference between

Table 1: **Red Kite biometrics**
(from Baker (1993) and Ferguson-Lees & Christie (2001); measurements are averages and ranges in centimetres with sample size in brackets where relevant)

	Male		Female	
Body length	60-72		60-72	
Wingspan	143-171		143-171	
Wing length[1]	49.0, 44.8-53.2	(7)	50.5, 47.8-53.5	(20)
Tail length	32.7, 30.1-35.1	(5)	34.3, 31.4-37.6	(15)
Bill	2.74, 2.58-2.92	(7)	2.77, 2.56-2.99	(19)
Tarsus length	5.32, 5.20-5.50	(4)	5.28, 5.10-5.40	(9)
Claw	2.22, 2.13-2.26	(3)	2.19, 2.06-2.38	(9)

[1] From carpal joint to wing tip

the sexes, it is the male that is bigger than the female. Reversed size dimorphism is at its most extreme in the Sparrowhawk, where females can be up to 25% larger than males and twice as heavy. In contrast, there is little difference in size and weight between male and female Red Kites, although females tend to be slightly larger and heavier on average (Table 1).

According to Baker (1993) birds weighing less than 0.95kg are likely to be males, whilst those above 1.23kg are probably females. Most, however, fall between these weights and therefore cannot be reliably separated, even in the hand. A sample of birds, about 12 weeks old, were weighed before release in central England. Twelve males (sexed from DNA in blood samples) ranged from 0.72 to 0.91kg with an average of 0.80kg, and 14 females ranged from 0.8 to 1.01kg, averaging 0.87kg. These figures are somewhat lower than those given by Baker, which is probably because the birds were youngsters, yet to make their first flight. Ferguson-Lees and Christie (2001) gave weight ranges of 0.76-1.22kg for full-grown males and 0.96-1.60kg for females, and suggested that birds were, on average, heavier in the winter period (October-March) than during the summer. Although there is a degree of overlap in size it is occasionally possible to separate the sexes in the field at close range, when the male and female are seen together. When, for example, a pair are circling together over a breeding site, the slight difference in size and build between the two may be apparent.

Newton (1979) showed that size differences between the sexes are generally greatest in species that rely on the active hunting of live prey, and suggested that this allowed food resources to be partitioned. Female Sparrowhawks, for example, are able to capture considerably larger prey than males. In carrion feeding species, where the prey is not killed, such partitioning of food by size is not feasible, as, even if females were much larger than males, they would not gain access to new, larger, sources of food. The Red Kite is predominantly a scavenger but does, at times, also take live prey and so the small difference in size between the sexes fits well with Newton's ideas. The reason why it is the female rather than the male that is the larger of the sexes in birds of prey is perhaps most likely to relate to the greater amount of time spent at the nest and hence her greater role in defending the nest and its contents from potential predators (Newton 1979).

Taxonomy

The Red Kite's closest relative and the only other species within the genus *Milvus* is the Black Kite *Milvus migrans*. Recent genetic work has suggested that they diverged as separate species only relatively recently, perhaps in one of the glaciations of the Pleistocene period, between 129,000 and 645,000 years ago (Roques & Negro 2005). These two 'sister species' share many similarities in appearance and behaviour, and even hybridise occasionally, producing offspring with features of both species. Hybrid pairs have been reported in Italy, Sweden and Germany, and Ortlieb's book *Der Rotmilan* (1989) includes photographs of a hybrid pair and an example of the resultant offspring. In 2005, Brian Etheridge found a male Black Kite paired with a female Red Kite in northern Scotland and this pair bred successfully in 2006. It has not been confirmed that the Black Kite is the genetic father of the young (and the chicks appeared identical to Red Kites) although he was seen bringing food to the nest.

The term 'kite' has been applied to a large number of birds of prey throughout the world, although many are not closely related to each other or indeed to the Red Kite. Ferguson-Lees and Christie (2001) followed previous authors in including 17 different genera of birds within the 'kite' grouping, describing them as a 'particularly heterogeneous collection'. For example, although the Square-tailed and Black-breasted Kites of Australia share some of the plumage and behavioural characteristics of the Red Kite, they are not thought to be closely related. For some species, including the American White-tailed, Mississippi and Snail Kites, it is no doubt the shared features of long wings and long, sometimes forked or notched, tail that has resulted in the use of 'kite' in the common names. Recent genetic studies have suggested that the Brahminy Kite found in India, Indonesia and Australasia, and the Whistling Kite of Australasia, both in the *Haliastur* genus, are actually the closest relatives of Red and Black Kites (Wink & Sauer-Gürth 2004). Buzzards in the genus *Buteo*, including the Common Buzzard, and sea-eagles in the genus *Haliaeetus*, including the White-tailed Sea Eagle, are also thought to be closely related to the two *Milvus* kites.

The Cape Verde Kite

There has been considerable uncertainty as to the status of the Cape Verde Kite *Milvus milvus fasciicauda*, which is (or was) found only on this Atlantic island group. It has variously been proposed that it represents a race of Red Kite (distinct from the *milvus* race that occurs across the rest of the range), a separate species in its own right, or even a hybrid between Red and Black Kite. Hazevoet (1995) examined 32 museum specimens of birds taken from Cape Verde that had previously been identified as Red Kites. He classed 25 as *fasciicauda*, six as Black Kites (which were also known to occur on the islands) and one as a hybrid between the two.

In an attempt to clarify the relationships of *fasciicauda* and to help save this 'form' from extinction, a search of the islands was undertaken in 2002 and five unidentified kites were taken into captivity (Johnson *et al*. 2005). A genetic analysis was undertaken comparing these birds to historical museum specimens known to have been taken from the Cape Verde Islands. The results showed that the historical specimens were not genetically distinct from the Red Kites found elsewhere in Europe, and the Cape Verde Kite could not therefore be considered as a viable species, or even sub-species, in its own right. The results suggest that either the islands were colonised by Red Kites only relatively recently or (less likely) that there was continuous interchange of individuals (and so genetic material) between the Cape Verde population and the European population (Crochet 2006a). The genetic work also showed that the five birds caught in 2002 all contained Black Kite DNA, although it was not clear whether these birds were pure Black Kites or hybrids between Black and Red Kites. It is a sobering thought that the mystery has now been, at least partially, solved, just at the time when the Cape Verde Kite appears to have become extinct in the wild.

Birds that formerly occurred on the Canary Islands and birds from populations of the nominate *milvus* race in North Africa, have been reported to be smaller than those in Europe (Glutz von Blotzheim *et al*. 1971), although there has been no recent confirmation of this.

Local names

The word 'kite' is derived from the Anglo-Saxon 'cyta'. It has been suggested that 'cyta' is onomatopoeic of the bird's call or, alternatively, it may have been derived from the Aryan 'skut' - to shoot, go swiftly - a presumed reference to the bird's wheeling and swooping flight. 'Kite' evolved to its present day form from 'cyta' through the medieval word 'kyte' (Macleod 1954). An alternative name that is even older than 'kyte' is 'glede' or 'glead', derived from the old

Saxon verb for gliding, but this has long since fallen into disuse. There is often confusion as to the exact meaning of the term 'kyte' in the 17th and 18th centuries as, in some areas, this word was used to denote any large bird of prey. To make matters even more complicated, 'kitt' or 'keat' was used for Buzzard in Devon, where the Red Kite was known exclusively as 'glede', and, in Ireland, 'kite' was used locally for Buzzard and for both Hen and Marsh Harriers. 'Puttock' is another name that was commonly used for both Red Kite and Buzzard, predominantly in the Midlands and the eastern counties, although Shakespeare used it when referring specifically to the Red Kite. It has been variously suggested that this name is a contraction of 'Poult-hawk', reflecting concerns about the predation of poultry, or that it is derived from an old English word meaning 'swooper' (Palin 2002). Other local names include 'scoul' (Cornwall), 'fork-tail' (Yorkshire), 'crotch-tail' (Essex) and Greedy Gled (northern England). Variants on the old name of glede or glead survive today in place names such as Gladsmuir in East Lothian and Glede Knowe near Innerleithen in the Scottish Borders (Minns & Gilbert 2001), although it is impossible to rule out Marsh or Hen Harriers in such references as both species have historically been known by these names (Bolam 1912).

The standard Welsh language name for the Red Kite is 'barcud' although, as elsewhere, many local names were used in the past. 'Hebog cwt-fforchog' roughly translates as forked-tailed bird of prey and the beautifully descriptive 'boda wennol', which was used in the Tywi valley and elsewhere, means swallow-hawk (Lovegrove 1990). In Scotland and Ireland there are many Gaelic names for the Red Kite including 'croman-cearc' (chicken-hawk) and 'croman lochaidh' (hawk of the sheep's fleece!). One of the Irish names listed by D'Arcy (1999) is 'préachán ceartach' which translates as rag or cloth kite and is no doubt a reference to the bird's habit of incorporating this material into its nest.

Chapter 2

HISTORY IN BRITAIN

Over the centuries, the fluctuating fortunes of the Red Kite in Britain have, perhaps more than any other bird, been bound together with human activities and changing public attitudes. Until around 2,500 BC, when Neolithic man began to clear significant areas of the wildwood then covering most of Britain, birds requiring open country must have been rare or absent. The Red Kite, although dependent on woodland for nest and roost sites, spends the majority of its time, and finds almost all of its food, by foraging over open ground. As more and more land was cleared for agriculture, so the resulting patchwork landscape of small woods and fields became ever more suitable and, by Norman times, the Red Kite was probably one of our most widespread and familiar birds. From this high point, numbers were drastically reduced at the hands of humans, before changing attitudes, intensive conservation efforts and a certain amount of good fortune came just in time to prevent extinction.

Early history and medieval Britain

In the 8th century the Red Kite was one of only 11 species of British bird to have been specifically recorded in literature, along with birds such as Raven, White-tailed Sea Eagle and Goshawk (Palmer 2000). A description of a Red Kite stealing a bone from two dogs is included in Chaucer's *The Knights Tale* of 1390, and its scavenging habits are also referred to by William Turner (1544) in his *Avium Principarum* (the first ever written account of birds in Britain), where he lists birds previously named by Aristotle (BC 384-322) and Pliny (AD 23-79).

In medieval times, the Red Kite would certainly have been a common sight wheeling low over the open countryside. It would also have been familiar to those living in some of our larger towns and cities, including London, where it foraged by scavenging amongst refuse and animal waste on the filthy, unpaved streets. By the 15th century, visitors were commenting on the tameness and size of Red Kite flocks in London, and reporting how food, including bread and butter, was even snatched from the hands of small children (Reid-Henry & Harrison 1988). The boldness of the bird is evident from a much later account by Colonel G. Montagu, writing in 1833:

> *A poor woman was washing some entrails in a stream of water, part of which extended a few yards out of the basket placed in the water: the hungry bird had long been hovering, viewing with anxious eye so delicious a bait, and took the opportunity of actually pouncing upon and carrying off a part, in spite of all the woman's efforts with hand and tongue, the latter of which might have alarmed a more powerful enemy.*

In parts of present-day Asia and Africa it is the Black Kite that fulfils the role of urban scavenger and this has led some to suggest that it was this species, and not the Red Kite, that occurred in our medieval towns (Dawson 1988). There is no evidence to support this claim and, to the contrary, descriptions of birds from visitors to London familiar with both species demonstrate beyond reasonable doubt that it was the Red Kite that thrived in medieval Britain. For example,

DAN POWELL

William Turner (1544) clearly distinguished between the two species and stated that he had only seen the Red Kite in Britain. The Flemish naturalist Charles Clusius visited England in 1571 and subsequently described the birds he saw in London as residents. If they had been Black Kites, they would presumably have been summer visitors as is the case in this species' European range today. The Black Kite has almost certainly never been anything other than a rare summer visitor to Britain.

Red Kites could only survive in urban areas because standards of sanitation in those days were poor. Animal waste, simply thrown out onto the streets, provided an abundant source of food. Scavenging by Red Kites, and also Ravens, helped to remove waste and so reduced the risk to human health from outbreaks of disease. In recognition of this street-cleaning role, both species were granted special protection in England and Wales under royal statute from the 15th century onwards, the first species to be protected for reasons other than hunting. The same protection did not extend to Scotland where James II, as early as 1457, encouraged the destruction of 'Kites' and other species (Lovegrove 1990), a portent of what was to come throughout Britain.

The Red Kite in falconry

In Spain the Red Kite is known as Milano Real, or Royal Kite, and in France and Italy the names of Milan Royal and Nibbio Reale have the same meaning. These names do not refer to the majesty of the bird itself but rather to the pleasure it provided to royal hunting parties in the Middle Ages. Because of its accomplished all-round flying skills and habit of circling high in the air, royal falconers considered that the taking of a Red Kite was the very peak of achievement for a trained falcon. Only the larger falcons such as Lanners from North Africa and the Middle East, and possibly Gyr Falcons, could manage such a feat. Yarrell (1857) describes how an owl with a Fox's tail tied to its leg to impede its flight was trained to fly around in circles, acting as a decoy in order to attract a Red Kite to within range of the falconer's bird.

There appears to have been considerable rivalry between the English and French in this sport and James I was apparently prepared to spend as much as £1,000 in acquiring a cast of birds that could outdo the achievements of the French. Unfortunately, at a specially arranged demonstration that took place near Royston in Hertfordshire, the first Red Kite pursued rose to such a height that neither it or the trained falcon were ever seen again (Lovegrove 1990).

A decline in fortunes

The Red Kite's rapid downturn in fortunes occurred, for different reasons, in both urban areas and in the countryside. In towns and cities, where they had taken advantage of the filth and squalor of the medieval period, sanitation inevitably improved until there was very little left for the birds to eat. The last remaining breeding pair in London was recorded at Grey's Inn in 1777, although the odd bird was seen over the town well into the 1800s (Lovegrove 1990).

The situation was no better in rural areas where the Red Kite was blamed for taking free-range chickens and even livestock and, for this reason, had probably never been much appreciated by country dwellers. Along with other birds of prey and predatory mammals it was increasingly heavily persecuted as rural settlements grew and the human population increased. Unfortunately, with its scavenging lifestyle and relative lack of fear of people, the Red Kite was a very easy bird to kill. Poisoning, in particular, was a highly effective, although totally indiscriminate, means of control and, as the Red Kite is very much a social species, a single bait would often have been enough to account for several birds. Traps, baited with animal carcasses or live prey were also used.

A variety of traps were employed for catching Red Kites and other species as early as the 16th century

The role of persecution

The decline of the Red Kite was so rapid during the 18th and early 19th centuries that some authors believed that persecution alone could not be responsible. Lilford (1883) suggested that a very severe winter might have caused the declines he noted in Northamptonshire and reported the views of a correspondent, while doubting them himself, that the draining of the fens might have been a factor in neighbouring Cambridgeshire. Harvie-Brown (1906) even suggested that the loss of many large trees to storms in the early 19th century could have reduced the availability of nesting sites. More recently, Shrubb (2003) expressed the view that the enclosure and partitioning of farmland in the 18th century, and a resulting reduction in livestock mortality formerly associated with large open areas, was at least partly responsible for the rapid loss of the Red Kite, in addition to the loss of the Buzzard and Raven from many areas.

It is possible that such factors did affect Red Kite populations at a local level but it is equally clear that it was widespread persecution that played by far the greatest role in the bird's demise. Ticehurst (1934), writing about 'vermin' control in the parish of Tenterden, Kent describes just how common the Red Kite must once have been and gives a vivid impression of the scale of the subsequent destruction (see below). The reference to payment relates to the 1566 'Acte for the Preservacion of Grayne' which offered rewards for the heads of 'noyfull Fowles and Vermyn' in order to encourage their destruction.

The Kite. . . . . .was evidently a very numerous species and one or more of these grand birds must have been a commonplace everyday sight as they soared over the surrounding forest that formed such a suitable home for them. Between 1654 and 1675 an average of not much more than two a year were paid for, but during the next decade it becomes evident how common the bird must have been, for during this time no fewer than 380 were accounted for, with a maximum of 100 in a single year. It sounds incredible in these days, and there is not much cause for wonderment in the fact that, though no slackening in the general campaign is manifest, the numbers of Kites killed in the next two years dropped to thirteen and two respectively. If the same sort of thing was going on in other Wealden parishes, no large raptorial bird could have long withstood such a drain on its numbers and it is no surprise that we no longer have any Kites with us.

The birds and mammals listed in the 1566 act included such relatively innocuous species as the Hedgehog, Bullfinch, woodpeckers, and, of course, the unfortunate Red Kite. Churchwardens were responsible for making the payments and often kept detailed parish records. In some areas the payment rate for each Red Kite was one penny, the same as for crows but only half the amount paid for each Buzzard or Stoat. This suggests either that the Red Kite was so common and easy to kill that only a small reward was deemed necessary, or perhaps that it was considered to be less of a threat than some other species. The following extracts are from the churchwarden's records for the parish of Tenterden, as reported by Ticehurst (1934), detailing payments in pounds, shillings and pence:

1667-68
Paid to Thomas Jonas for 4 Raven's heads and 1 Hedgehogg's head

　　　　　　　　　　　　　　　　　　　　　　　　　　　　　0　0　4
To John Drew for 1 dozen of Crowe's heads and for 3 Kytes . . . .

　　　　　　　　　　　　　　　　　　　　　　　　　　　　　0　0　8
To Wm. Baker for 4 Kytes, 1 Pulcat and 4 Raven's heads . . . .　*0　1　2*
To John Morphett for 2 Kyte's heads, 4 Woodpeckers and 8 Crowe's
heads . . . .　*0　0　10*

1676-77
Ffrancis Peck for 3 dozen & halfe of Kyte's heads and
1 Hedghogg's head . . . .　*0　1　1*

Ticehurst suspected that the 1676-77 record, involving payment to one person for no less than 42 Red Kite heads, probably related to nestlings rather than adults, citing the lower than usual level of payment for each individual bird. He also pointed out that this would represent the contents of approximately 15-20 nests using a rough average of 2-3 young per nest. It is interesting that, although records of bounty payments have been discovered for many areas of England and Scotland, there are apparently none for Wales, where the Red Kite eventually found its last refuge in Britain.

Records from another part of the country show that persecution continued apace into the 19th century (Table 2), this time, with a new justification - the protection of gamebirds for shooting. The rearing and release of gamebirds on large sporting estates increased in popularity during the late 18th century and species seen as potential gamebird predators were simply not tolerated. Game-keepers were employed with predator control as one of their main responsibilities and birds of prey were targeted with an almost religious fervour that the already depleted and vulnerable Red Kite could not withstand for long. The Marquess of Bute in 1808 went as far as preparing the following oath to be taken by gamekeepers on his estates in Argyll, Scotland (Richmond 1959):

. . . . . . and finally I shall use my best endeavours to destroy all birds of prey etc, with their nests, wherever they can be found therein. So help me God.

Table 2: **Birds and mammals killed on the Burley Estate, Rutland, 1807-1816** *(from Squires & Jeeves 1994)*

Red Kites	183	Woodpeckers	103
Buzzards	285	Stoats	1,269
Hawks	340	Weasels	454
Owls	386	Polecats	206
Magpies	1,530	Pine Martins	9
Jays	428	Cats	554
Crows	1,603	Red Squirrels	197
Jackdaws	1,798	Rats	17,108
Herons	24		

As well as using traps and poison baits, gamekeepers in the 19th century had a further option for controlling predators. The shotgun had evolved gradually since first developed for shooting game in the 16th century and was an increasingly effective weapon against birds of prey. The Red Kite's slow, languid foraging flights, often low over the ground, and its relative lack of fear of humans, made it a particularly easy target for guns of ever improving accuracy. As numbers continued to fall, the Red Kite became an increasing target for egg collectors and the taxidermy trade. The value of its eggs and skins increased as a direct result of increasing rarity, offering ever greater financial incentives for collectors to pursue the bird, and driving it relentlessly towards extinction. Despite all these pressures, Latham (1821-28) reported that the Red Kite was still "very common in England" and as late as 1833, Montagu believed that it was still "common in the eastern parts". Yet, by now, the bird was in very steep decline. By the 1840s the Red Kite was no longer breeding in many English counties and in the following 30-40 years it was lost from the remainder (Brown & Grice 2005) and from all of Scotland. It is perhaps no surprise that one of the last breeding records in England involved a female shot at its nest (near Bishop's Castle, Shropshire in 1863), while one of the last breeding pairs in Scotland (in Caithness, 1884) had its eggs taken and presented to the British Museum (Holloway 1996). Only in Wales did a handful of the 'old-race' of British Red Kites remain by the end of the 19th century.

The Red Kite in Wales

In the remote valleys of central Wales, away from the major sporting estates, the Red Kite clung on to a last refuge in Britain, hampered by the unproductive nature of the land, the unsuitable damp, cold summers and continued persecution, albeit at a lower level than previously found in England and Scotland. It was initially thought that the population reached its lowest level in about 1905 and

that only about five birds remained, but it is now known that numbers were always somewhat higher than this and the true low-point was not until some three decades later. Peter Davis has managed to piece together a reasonably complete picture of the Red Kite's changing fortunes in the first half of the 20th century using the diaries and unpublished accounts of those involved in protecting the bird in Wales at the time, notably Professor J.F. Salter, Col. Morrey Salmon and E.G.B Meade-Waldo (Davis 1993). From these records it seems likely that at no time did the population fall much below ten territorial pairs and the total spring population, including immatures and unmated adults, was probably always higher than 20 individuals. An estimated population of 20 territorial pairs in the 1890s declined gradually to a low of about ten pairs in the 1930s and early 1940s before the start of a slow recovery, which continues to this day.

Whilst initially, this new information suggests that the Red Kite did not come quite as close to extinction as had previously been thought, recent genetic evidence, utilising sections of maternally inherited DNA, has helped to reveal a rather different picture. Blood samples taken from Welsh Red Kites in the late 1980s were analysed by researchers at Nottingham University (May *et al.* 1993a) and showed that, until relatively recently, all Red Kites in Wales were probably descended from just a single breeding female that passed through the genetic bottleneck when the population was at its lowest ebb. Although the total population probably did not fall below ten territorial pairs it seems that, at the low point, only a single breeding pair reared young that survived and contributed to population expansion in later years. The British population was therefore almost as close as it is possible to get to becoming extinct!

Genetic work has also shown that, at some point, an immigrant female joined the Welsh population. The new blood-line, detected in the DNA samples, corresponded closely to one found commonly in central European Red Kites and it is thought most likely that this was the origin of the immigrant (May *et al.* 1993a).

Red Kite protection in Wales – the early years

Although Red Kites survived in central Wales as a result of lower levels of human persecution and interference, they were by no means totally free from such molestations, and, by the end of the 19th century, there was an urgent need for active protection of the remaining pairs. The story of Red Kite protection in Wales is a long and complex one, spanning more than 100 years. It is probably the longest-running active bird protection scheme that has ever been carried out. Roger Lovegrove in his book *The Kite's Tale* (1990), upon which the account below is partly based, described the often convoluted and rarely uncontroversial events in some detail, making no attempt to hide the less savoury aspects of the period:

> *In a story as notable as this, it would be satisfying to be able to record the smooth and efficient progress of the successive schemes as the story evolved over the years. However, [one] of the remarkable aspects of Kite protection has been the extent to which it has been plagued over the years by bitter division, acrimonious clashes of personality, jealousies, intrigue and deception.*

Some of the earliest efforts to protect Red Kites were led by Alfred Gwynne Vaughan and the Rev. David Edmondes Owen in Breconshire and Radnorshire, starting around 1890, and including the production of 'Instructions to Keepers', circulated via local landowners. These individuals were the first to place barbed wire on trees in order to discourage the nests from being robbed, and also introduced bounty payments for landowners willing to protect breeding pairs on their land (Cross & Davis 2005). The system of bounty payments was to be a mainstay of protection for the greater part of the 20th century, and a constant reminder of just how much attitudes had changed since the days when financial rewards were offered for the destruction of Red Kites. Despite these efforts, continuing losses to unsympathetic gamekeepers and egg collectors, including nest robberies by some individuals supposedly involved in the protection scheme, led to the cessation of breeding in the county of Breconshire by 1909. There were similar problems in other counties, including north Radnor, where birds faced an additional threat. Here, nestlings taken from local nests were reared in captivity and offered for sale to travellers on the stagecoach to Aberystwyth. There was an apparently lively trade in nestlings in several areas with each bird reputed to be worth between one and five guineas. One nestling was even reported to have been exchanged for a bicycle in the late 1800s! (Peter Davis in litt.).

In 1903 the highly respected British Ornithologists' Club (BOC) became involved in Red Kite protection, passing a motion of censure on any member found to be involved in taking eggs, and helping to set up the first official 'Kite Committee'. During such a critical period, every breeding failure increased the chance that the population would be lost completely. Although the details are rather sketchy, it is thought that around this time, the Royal Society for the Protection of Birds (RSPB) also became involved for the first time, donating money to a 'Kite Preservation Fund' so that bounties could be paid, and helping to organise an influential 'Kite Watchers' Committee'.

The involvement of John Walpole-Bond, a well known egg collector, in the protection scheme during this period was highly ambiguous. Although he claimed to be an active participant in the scheme, it is clear from his diaries that he was aware, each year, of several nests whose whereabouts were not divulged to the BOC or its local representatives (Cross & Davis 2005). Even harder to understand was an incident involving the respected ornithologist, but inveterate egg collector, Desmond Nethersole-Thompson, in 1930. He not only took a clutch of Welsh Red Kite eggs from the Tywi valley but, a year later, openly exhibited them at a meeting of the British Oologists Association causing a storm of protest and even resignations from members appalled by such an action. A long and acrimonious correspondence continued in the press for several years, much of it conducted by Nethersole-Thompson himself under a nom-de-plume. In 1937, another paid 'Kite Watcher' was found to have written to a Guildford egg collector, offering him a clutch of three eggs for £8, in what was certainly not an isolated occurrence.

Reinforcements from Spain

In East Radnorshire, close to the border with England, the period between the late 1920s and the mid-1940s produced reports of considerable numbers of Red Kites and rumours of several nests. It was first thought that this represented a welcome natural expansion of the native population into a new area but now seems most likely to have been the result of an early attempt to reinforce the Welsh population, carried out by C.H. Gowland, an egg-dealer from Liverpool

(Davis 1993). Gowland apparently imported batches of Red Kite eggs from Spain in 1927-28 and again in 1934-35 and had them placed in Buzzard nests in the Builth Wells area (Gowland 1947). Red Kites in Spain tend to lay several weeks earlier than Welsh Buzzards and it is far from clear how the eggs were kept viable before they could be placed in the foster nests. Some reports suggest that, despite the difficulties, many of these eggs did hatch. Unfortunately, no records were kept and there is no indication of subsequent survival rates. If young did indeed fledge from nests as a result of these efforts, it would certainly be interesting to know how they fared in the wild having been reared to independence by adults of another species.

Capt H.A. Gilbert made a further attempt to reinforce the population in the 1950s, this time by placing a single clutch of Spanish eggs in a Radnorshire Buzzard nest. The clutch of three eggs apparently failed to hatch but, undeterred, Gilbert arranged for two young Spanish Red Kites to be imported from near Algeciras in southern Spain. Diego and Pepa (as named by their Spanish collector) were kept in captivity until the following summer before being released (Gilbert 1957). They are reported to have remained in the area for at least a few months but their ultimate fate is not known. The process was repeated with two further birds in the following year. These were released in the spring of 1959 having been in captivity over the previous winter and apparently remained in the area for a few weeks before disappearing (Lovegrove 1990). Well-monitored releases in England and Scotland, undertaken as part of an ongoing reintroduction programme (Chapter 5), have shown that released Red Kites fare better in the wild if held in captivity for as short a period as possible. It is perhaps unlikely that Gilbert's birds, held in aviaries for approximately one year, survived for long enough to join the Welsh breeding population. There is no evidence that any of the Spanish stock involved in the various reinforcement projects survived for long enough to breed. The Radnor records petered out during the 1940s (Davis 1993) and genetic profiling of Red Kites in Wales carried out in the 1990s did not reveal any evidence of Spanish blood in the Welsh population (May et al. 1993a, 1993b).

The road to recovery

The Second World War seems to have marked a turning point in the Red Kite's fortunes, probably helped by wartime travel restrictions limiting the potential for interference with nests, and a reduction in persecution while gamekeepers were away fighting. Although, for the same reasons, there is an incomplete picture of the population size during the war years, by the end of the 1940s it was clear that Red Kites were breeding in new areas away from the small core population in the Tywi valley. By the early 1950s the breeding population had crept above ten pairs and ten or more young fledged in most years. There is a suggestion that the outbreak of myxomatosis in 1954 had an adverse effect by reducing the number of Rabbits, one of the Red Kite's main food sources. Although the number of breeding pairs remained above ten during the second half of the 1950s, breeding success was poor and far fewer young were fledged.

During the 1960s an informal 'Kite' group led by Capt H.R.H. Vaughan oversaw a steady increase in numbers to 27 known pairs by the time a new official 'Kite Committee' met for the first time in 1971. The RSPB and Nature Conservancy Council (NCC) were instrumental in forming the committee and were able to provide increased resources for protection, as well as instigating a full programme of research to enable the main threats to Welsh Red Kites to be identified and tackled. The RSPB further demonstrated its commitment to preserving Red Kites by purchasing substantial areas of land used by breeding pairs within the Tywi valley. The continued increase in the population was greatly helped by changing public attitudes, with a growing attachment to the bird as a symbol of Welsh individuality and ever increasing support for measures to help protect breeding pairs. The birds also benefited from novel techniques such as the 'rescuing' of eggs known to be at risk from egg collectors and subsequent return to the wild of the young hatched in captivity (see Chapter 11).

There were to be further setbacks during the next few decades but, in general, a steady increase in numbers has been maintained right up to the present day. In recent years the rate of population growth has increased, probably as a result of Red Kites moving into areas of more fertile countryside where breeding productivity is higher, and because of continuing reductions in illegal persecution.

Into the 21st century

By the mid-1990s, the Welsh population had increased to well over 100 breeding pairs and Red Kites enjoyed an increasingly high public profile. 'Kite Country', an eco-tourism initiative funded by local authorities and the European Union, was set up in 1994 and was soon helping to attract large numbers of visitors to mid-Wales to see Red Kites. As part of the initiative, visitor centres were established, some with live video-links to nests during the breeding season. Public viewing facilities were also set up at several sites, the most successful attracting anything up to 100 birds by providing food at the same time each day. For a small payment, visitors could now enjoy superb close up views of Red Kites, not to mention Buzzards and Ravens, from purpose-built hides.

A downside to the success story in Wales has been the reduction in funding for the protection and monitoring of a species no longer seen as such a high priority for limited conservation funds. The RSPB and Countryside Council for Wales (formerly NCC) reluctantly concluded that the money spent on monitoring Red Kites in Wales was needed elsewhere. Most of the income derived from feeding centres and similar initiatives goes directly to those involved in the tourism industry rather than to funding the conservation or monitoring of the Red Kite population in Wales.

Many people involved in Red Kite conservation felt that the reduction in funding for monitoring work was a little premature, particularly at a time when so many more tourists were coming to mid-Wales, and the potential for disturbance was increasing. There was also a feeling that the detailed, long-term monitoring of the population, a unique and valuable record of a rare species recovering from the brink of extinction, should be maintained for as long as possible. As a result of such concerns, the Welsh Kite Trust, a registered charity, was set up in 1996 by a group of individuals with a long history of involvement in Red Kite conservation. It continues, to this day, to coordinate monitoring work and provide advice and guidance on all aspects of Red Kite conservation in Wales.

England and Scotland

During the 20th century the Red Kite became an increasingly regular visitor to England and, to a lesser extent, Scotland, particularly in eastern counties. Records involved a combination of displaced continental migrants and dispersing young from both the continent and from central Wales. The pattern of steady increase is well shown by the historical records for Sussex (see Figure 1). It is thought that the Red Kite ceased to breed in the county sometime before 1825 and from then until the early 1970s the species was only a very scarce and irregular visitor. Only 18 birds were seen during the 94 years between 1843 and 1937, and there were then only three records in the following 24 years to 1961. From the late 1960s the number of records increased and the species became an annual visitor to the county. By the late 1980s as many as nine birds were recorded during a single year (1988), three times the number during the whole of the 1950s and 1960s (Hope 1996).

In Norfolk the change in status during the past 150 years has been even more dramatic. The last record in the 19th century was of a single bird shot at Winterton, on the east coast, in 1881 and now displayed in the Castle Museum, Norwich. It took a further 77 years for the species to be recorded again in the county, when, in 1958, three singles were seen. There was then a sustained increase during the next few decades with 16 birds in the 1960s, 34 in the 1970s

Figure 1: **Annual totals of Red Kites in Sussex, 1962-94** *(from Hope 1996)*

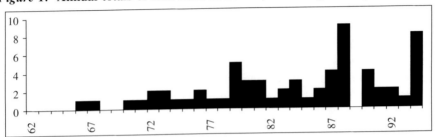

and 43 in the 1980s. The increase continued into the 1990s when wandering birds from the reintroduced populations contributed to the numbers recorded. In the spring of 1996 alone a glut of sightings was thought to have involved about 45 different individuals (Taylor *et al.* 1999). Inland counties too have seen a noticeable increase in records over the last few decades, although the numbers involved are far fewer than for eastern and southern coastal counties.

There are two main reasons for the dramatic increase in records during recent decades. Firstly, there have been substantial increases in Red Kite breeding populations, both in mid-Wales and in parts of northern Europe, from where the majority of wandering birds or displaced migrants probably originate. Secondly, there has been a rapid increase in the popularity of birdwatching since the early 1960s and, with more observers on the ground, more of the birds that wander from their breeding areas are likely to be recorded.

Before the start of the reintroduction programme, there were very few occasions in the 20th century when breeding is thought to have taken place outside of the core Welsh range, despite the rapidly increasing numbers of visiting birds. Young Red Kites, whilst prone to wander during their first year, usually return to their natal area when old enough to breed and, as with many other birds of prey, the Red Kite has shown a great reluctance to recolonise its former range. There have, however, been a few isolated records of pairs apparently settled on a territory in the spring in England. In 1912 and 1913, a pair was rumoured to have bred near Dartmeet in Devon (Brown & Grice 2005). In the late 1970s a summering bird was present at a site in Cumbria for two years running and a pair was reported to have bred in Cumbria 1981 (Stott *et al.* 2002) although the details required to confirm this are remarkably hard to come by. More recently, a pair thought most likely to have originated from central or northern Europe bred successfully in northeast Suffolk in 1996 and 1997 (Carter 1998). These breeding attempts proved, in all cases, to be isolated occurrences rather than the beginning of natural recolonisation. The Red Kite has now returned to parts of its former range in England and Scotland as a result of the translocation of young from areas of Europe where the species is still common. The full story of this, one of the most successful bird reintroduction programmes anywhere in the world, is told in Chapter 5.

Chapter 3

BREEDING DISTRIBUTION AND STATUS

The Red Kite's breeding range is almost entirely restricted to Europe, with only small populations found in North Africa and parts of the Middle East. From the 19th century or earlier, there was a steady decline across much of the range as a direct result of human persecution (Bijleveld 1974). The Red Kite has suffered more than most birds of prey at the hands of humans. Its association with human habitation, relative lack of fear of people and scavenging habits make it an easy bird to kill. In some countries, or regions within countries, Red Kites were reduced to very low levels or wiped out completely, as was the case in England and Scotland. The bird's adaptability meant that it still thrived in areas where persecution levels were low but the overall population was much reduced and the range fragmented. The decline has continued during the latter part of the 20th century in some areas, particularly in southern and eastern Europe where persecution remains a serious problem. To give some idea of the scale of the decline, Ferguson-Lees & Christie (2001) suggested that the breeding range probably extended over some 5-8 million km^2 of Europe in the 17th century but this has now been reduced to around 1.2 million km^2.

More encouragingly, in parts of central and north-western Europe, there have been substantial population increases and the Red Kite has regained some of its former range. Denmark, Belgium, the Czech Republic and Austria were all recolonised during 1970-1990 (Tucker & Heath 1994) and, as a result of the reintroduction programme, Red Kites are, once again, breeding in England and Scotland.

The rest of this chapter provides more details of the Red Kite's breeding status and distribution throughout its range. The information is based on the review carried out for the first edition of this book, together with a review recently undertaken by BirdLife International (2004), and other sources of information, where appropriate.

Figure 2: **World range of the Red Kite**

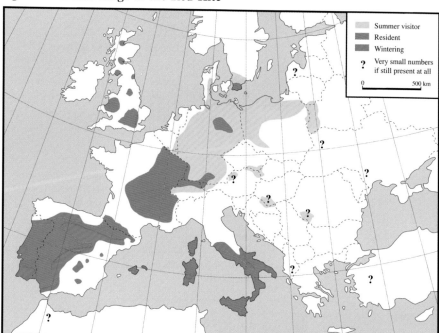

Table 3: **Breeding populations and trends**

Country/ Island	Breeding pairs and year – from Carter (2001)	Breeding pairs and year – from BirdLife International (2004)	Trend since 1990[1]	Additional data sources
Austria	10-15 (mid-1990s) 3-5 (1999)	5-10 (1998-02)	Increase	Gamauf (1995), Andreas Ranner (pers. comm.)
Belarus	<10 (1990)	3-10 (mid-1990s)	Stable?	Tucker & Heath (1994)
Belgium	50-60 (mid-1990s)	50-80 (1995-02)	Increase	Snow & Perrins (1998)
Canary Islands	Extinct by early 1970s			Blanco & González (1992)
Cape Verde Islands	5-6 individuals (1996-97)		Decline to extinction	Hille (1998), see text
Corsica	100-180 (late 1980s)		Increase to 208-277 pairs by 2002	Patrimonio (1990), Thiollay & Bretagnolle (2004)
Czech Republic	30-50 (1993-94)	70-100 (2000)	Increase	Snow & Perrins (1998)
Denmark	21 (1998)	17-22 (2001-02)	Stable/ decline	Sharrock & Davies (2000), Grell (2003)
England	131 (2000)		Increase to over 400 pairs by 2006	Wotton *et al.* (2002), see Chapter 5
France	2,300-2,900 (1982) 2,250-4,200 (mid-1990s)	3,000-3,800 (2000-02)	Decline	Thiollay & Terrasse (1984), Viñuela (1996), Rocamora & Yeatmann-Berthelot (1999), Thiollay *et al.* (in press)
Germany	9,000-12,000 (1999)	10,500-14,000 (late 1990s)	Decline	Tucker & Heath (1994), Mebs (1995), Mammen & Opitz (2000)
Hungary	1+ (late 1990s)	4-10 (1997-02)	Increase	Szabolcs Kókay (pers. comm.)

Table 3: **Breeding populations and trends** *(continued)*

Country/ Island	Breeding pairs and year – from Carter (2001)	Breeding pairs and year – from BirdLife International (2004)	Trend since 1990[1]	Additional data sources
Italy	220-250 (late 1990s)	300-400 (2003)	Stable?	Corso *et al*. (1999)
Latvia	<3 (late 1980s)	0-3 (1990s)	?	Evans & Pienkowski (1991), Tucker & Heath (1994)
Lithuania	<3 (late 1980s)	1-10 (1999-01)	?	Evans & Pienkowski (1991), Tucker & Heath (1994)
Luxembourg	46 territorial pairs (1997)	35-45 (2002)	Stable?	Conzemius (1998)
Majorca	27 (mid-1990s)		Decline	Viñuela *et al*. (1999)
Minorca	135 (late 1980s) 8 (1998)		Decline	Viñuela *et al*. (1999)
Moldova	1 (1990)	Absent (2000)		Tucker & Heath (1994)
Morocco	10-100 (early 1980s)		Decline?	Snow & Perrins (1998)
Netherlands	<5 (late 1990s)	0-1 (1998-2000)		Van den Berg & Bosman (1999), SOVON (2002)
Poland	400-500 (early 1990s)	650-700 (1998)	Increase	Adamski (1995)
Portugal	100-200 (mid-1990s)	50-100 (2002)	Decline	Viñuela (1996)
Romania	1-10 (early 1990s) 15-20 (1995)	0-5 (1995-02)	Decline	Snow & Perrins (1998), Tucker & Heath (1994), Zeitz *et al*. (1999)
Scotland	39 (2000)		Increase to 85 pairs by 2006	Wotton *et al*. (2002), see Chapter 5
Slovakia	10-20 (early 1990s)	15-20 (1980-99)	Stable?	Snow & Perrins (1998), Tucker & Heath (1994)
Spain	3,328-4,044 (1994)	1,900-2,700 (1998-02)	Decline to 2,000- 2,200 pairs by 2004	Viñuela *et al*. (1999), Cardiel (2006)

Table 3: **Breeding populations and trends** *(continued)*

Country/ Island	Breeding pairs and year – from Carter (2001)	Breeding pairs and year – from BirdLife International (2004)	Trend since 1990[1]	Additional data sources
Sweden	850 (1999)	800-850 (1999-00)	Increase	Kjellén (1999), Kjellén pers. comm.)
Switzerland	300-400 (early 1990s); 800-1,000 (mid-1990s)	800-1,200 (mid-1990s)	Increase	Müller (1995), Schmid *et al.* (1998)
Ukraine	5-8 (1990)	Absent (2000)	Decline	Viñuela (1994)
Wales	259 (2000)		Increase to 500-600 pairs by 2006	Wotton *et al.* (2002), Welsh Kite Trust newsletters
Yugoslavia (former)	<10 (1990s)	6-10 (1998-02)	Increase?	Snow & Perrins (1998)
Total	18,240-24,240	19,000-25,000	See text	

[1] The stated trend may differ from the two population estimates given in the table. This is usually the result of better information leading to a higher recent population estimate despite an actual decline in numbers, e.g. for Germany and Italy

Britain

The long-term decline, leading to extinction in England and Scotland, and reduction to only a handful of pairs in mid-Wales, was described in detail in the previous chapter. The Welsh population has increased steadily since the 1950s, with a more rapid rate of increase in recent years as the population has spread into more productive, food-rich countryside. In 2000, a comprehensive survey coordinated by the Welsh Kite Trust estimated the population at 259 breeding pairs (Wotton *et al.* 2002). Since then, the population has continued to increase rapidly and was estimated at 500-600 pairs in 2006, representing an annual rate of increase of about 15% in recent years (Tony Cross pers. comm.). Breeding birds were recorded in the following counties in 2006, in descending order of importance based on numbers of breeding pairs – Cardiganshire, Radnorshire, Carmarthenshire, Breconshire, Montgomeryshire, West Glamorgan, Pembrokeshire, Meirionnydd, Caernarvonshire, Monmouthshire, East Glamorgan and Denbighshire (Welsh Kite Trust newsletter, Autumn 2006). In 2004, the long-awaited recolonisation of western England occurred with a pair just over the border in Herefordshire rearing a single chick. This was consolidated the following year with two breeding pairs in the south Shropshire hills, as well as the returning Herefordshire pair (Welsh Kite Trust newsletters). There were also reports of a possible breeding attempt on Exmoor in Devon in 2006 which is most likely to be the result of Welsh birds spreading out from their traditional breeding areas.

A reintroduction programme started in England and Scotland in 1989, and, as a result, breeding has now taken place in a total of seven different areas as a direct result of local releases. Table 6 in Chapter 5 provides full details for each release project, together with the latest population estimate for the different areas. The total population in England now exceeds 400 pairs, with at least 85 pairs in Scotland. Illegal persecution remains a serious constraint to population expansion in Scotland and is the main reason for the lower number of breeding birds as compared with England (see Chapter 11 for more details).

Despite the success of the reintroduction programme, there has been only limited expansion of range away from the release areas and the vast majority of suitable countryside in England and Scotland remains unoccupied. Nevertheless, in recent years there have been encouraging signs that the birds are able to reach new areas, distant from the release sites, without further human assistance. Breeding has been recorded in a number of locations more than 30km from the nearest release site including Leicestershire, Lincolnshire, East Yorkshire, Hampshire, Hertfordshire, Sussex and Wiltshire. The extent to which these pioneering pairs are able to establish new breeding populations will have a major impact on how quickly the Red Kite is able to recolonise all of its former haunts in Britain.

A pair of untagged Red Kites that bred successfully in northeast Suffolk in 1996 and 1997 are thought most likely to have involved continental migrants rather than wandering birds from the reintroduction programme (Carter 1998). The lack of wing-tags does not prove a continental origin as many of the birds from the reintroduced populations at the time were also untagged. But the pair bred later than is typical for birds in Britain. The eggs were laid in early May which is more in line with the breeding period for birds in southern Sweden (Nils Kjellén pers. comm.). It was hoped that a small population would become established in this area but all five of the young reared during the two years dispersed and there have been no further breeding attempts since 1997.

It has been estimated that if the breeding densities currently found in southern England were to be replicated throughout the lowlands then the total English population alone would easily exceed 20,000 pairs (Carter & Grice 2000), not far short of the current world population. Whilst these numbers will not be reached for some time, given the currently small populations, there is no reason why they should not be achieved in the future.

Ireland

Evidence from archaeological remains and historical accounts suggest that the Red Kite was formerly widespread in Ireland, although, as a result of persecution, aided by the early clearance of forests, it was probably wiped out before the time when bird records were routinely kept. It is unlikely that it survived as a breeding bird into the 19th century (D'Arcy 1999). According to Cramp and Simmons (1980) a pair of Red Kites was present in the summer of 1976 but apparently they did not breed. In more recent times, the Red Kite has been an increasingly regular visitor to Ireland, in part as a result of wandering birds from the reintroduction programme in Scotland. At least one breeding attempt was made in Northern Ireland in 2002, and several apparent pairs have held territory in recent years, though no successful breeding has yet been recorded (Scott 2002). Reintroduction projects have now been proposed for both Northern Ireland and the Irish Republic, based on taking birds from Wales, and could start as early as 2007.

Central Europe

Several thousand years ago, when the majority of central Europe was covered with dense forest there would have been few opportunities for the Red Kite, dependent as it is on open country. However, the increasing importance of agriculture over the centuries helped to create a more suitable mixed landscape of open fields and woodland and, by the early 1800s, it had become a common and widespread bird across the region. Intense human persecution, particularly between 1850 and 1900, reduced numbers considerably, before protective legislation and changing attitudes led to a recovery (Ortlieb 1989).

A recent census of wintering Red Kites in Spain provides a rough indication of the number of breeding pairs in central Europe, the region from which Spain's wintering population is largely derived. The census estimated that, in 2004, 29,000-30,000 birds wintered in Spain, in addition to birds from the sedentary Spanish population (Cardiel 2006). This is a substantial and worrying decline from the estimate of 54,000-62,000 birds in a 1993/94 survey (Viñuela et al. 1999). Allowing for an average of 1.5 young for each breeding pair, and assuming that there are not high numbers of non-breeding birds, the latest survey suggests a migratory European population of around 8,000-9,000 pairs. This figure is somewhat lower than expected based on estimates of the breeding population in central European countries and perhaps reflects the fact that more birds are now wintering in central Europe rather than in Iberia.

Germany

Germany is by far the single most important country for breeding Red Kites. Recent estimates range from 9,000-14,000 pairs (Mammen & Opitz 2000, BirdLife International 2004) and although this is far lower than some earlier, and almost certainly exaggerated, estimates of up to 25,000 pairs, it still represents about half of the total world population. There were increases in some areas during the 1990s, but there have also been some worrying recent declines, particularly in the most important, higher density, areas of the breeding range. Declines have been blamed partly on improvements in waste disposal methods and also on a reduction in breeding productivity as a result of the intensification of farming methods, following German reunification and the entry of the former East Germany into the European Union (Hagemeijer & Blair 1997). However, the persecution of birds on their wintering grounds in Spain is perhaps the most important factor (Viñuela & Villafuerte 2003, Seoane et al. 2003) – see Chapter 11.

Switzerland

A healthy population in Switzerland at the end of the 19th century declined during the next 50 years until breeding was more or less confined to the Jura mountains. A breeding census in 1969 estimated the population at 90 pairs, rising to 235-300 pairs by the mid-1980s. By the early 1990s the population had increased further to an estimated 300-400 pairs, and occupied a range four times the size of that 25 years previously (Mosimann & Juillard 1988, Müller 1995). This dramatic rate of increase has been maintained and by the mid-late 1990s it was estimated that the population had reached 800-1,200 pairs (Schmid et al. 1998, BirdLife International 2004).

Austria

Austria once supported a healthy breeding population but this was lost as a result of intense persecution, mainly during the 19th century. Following a complete absence of breeding records in the 1950s and 1960s, recolonisation took place, probably as a result of immigration from Germany or Switzerland. There was a fairly slow increase to 10-15 pairs in the mid-1990s, concentrated along the Danube, March and Thaya rivers (Gamauf 1995). In recent years, the population may have declined once more, again probably as a result of persecution by hunters. The latest estimate covering the period 1998-2002 puts the population at 5-10 pairs (BirdLife International 2004).

Czech Republic

The Czech Republic is another central European country that has been recolonised in the recent past. By 1993/94 the population had increased to 30-50 pairs (Snow & Perrins 1998) with a further increase to 70-100 pairs by 2000 (BirdLife International 2004).

Scandinavia

Norway

Up until about 1880-1900, a small population existed in the far southeast of the country, close to the border with Sweden. Since then, the Red Kite has been only a rare visitor, with about 3-4 records annually in recent years, probably involving birds dispersing from the expanding populations in Sweden and Denmark.

Sweden

Human persecution reduced the number of Red Kites in Sweden to below 50 pairs during the 1960s. Since then, the population has increased steadily to an estimated 800-850 pairs by 1999-2000 (BirdLife International 2004, Nils Kjellén pers. comm.). The birds are concentrated in the province of Scania but have recently spread into neighbouring Halland and Blekinge. Productivity has remained high despite the increasing numbers and resulting higher breeding densities.

Denmark

The formerly large Danish population was persecuted to extinction by around 1910, although occasional breeding attempts occurred during the next 70 years (Grell 2003). In the 1970s the species became a regular breeder once again (Jørgensen 1989) and, by the early 1990s, the population had increased to 25-30 pairs. Disappointingly, the population declined slightly in the 1990s, probably as a result of a loss of birds due to pesticide poisoning. There were only 18 confirmed breeding pairs in 2002 (Grell 2003). The majority of pairs breed in southeast Jutland but pairs also occur all along the eastern side of the country and on at least two of the country's larger islands, including Bornholm to the southeast of Sweden (Grell 2003).

Northwest Europe

France

A survey carried out between 1979 and 1982 estimated that there were between 2,300 and 2,900 breeding pairs in France (Thiollay & Terrasse 1984). Overall, the population is thought to have been stable or increased slightly during the period 1970-90. More recently, the population was estimated at 3,000-3,800 breeding pairs, despite the fact that there have been significant declines in parts of the country during the past 10-15 years (BirdLife International 2004). Over 50% of the breeding population may have been lost in Alsace and losses are apparently even greater in Lorraine, Champagne-Ardenne, the Upper Loire Valley and Franche-Comté (J.M. Thiollay in litt., Rocamora & Yeatmann-Berthelot 1999). These losses have been attributed to a variety of causes including habitat loss, severe winter weather, a decline in the number of refuse dumps, and persecution. Poisoning is probably the major threat and Red Kites are affected by both legal poisoning campaigns carried out to control plagues of Common Voles, and illegal poison baits put out in order to control predatory birds and mammals. Nevertheless, the Red Kite remains reasonably common in many areas and following substantial declines in Spain, France may now support the largest breeding population of Red Kites after Germany.

Belgium

In Belgium, regular breeding ceased in the 1920s and did not resume until the 1970s (Snow & Perrins 1998). The population increased to 15-20 pairs during the 1980s with the majority of pairs in the east and southeast, and only sporadic breeding elsewhere. By the late 1990s the population was estimated at between 50 and 80 pairs (BirdLife International 2004).

Luxembourg

The population of Red Kites in this tiny country increased slowly from the 1940s to an average of about 12-15 pairs during the 1980s, with a maximum of 20 pairs in any one year. It was thought that this might represent the upper limit for the population but, by 1997, the range in the north had further expanded and the country as a whole supported 46 territories (Conzemius 1998).

The Netherlands

The Netherlands is on the north-western fringe of the Red Kite's range in continental Europe. There were no confirmed breeding records between 1852 and 1976 but low numbers of birds are now regularly present in the south and east, having spread from neighbouring Germany (Van den Berg & Bosman 1999). It is hoped that breeding pairs will become established in the near future.

Eastern Europe

Poland

Following a rapid decrease in the 19th and early 20th centuries, there has been a recent recovery in the Polish population, paralleling the increases in adjacent central European countries. In the early 1990s there were an estimated 400-500 pairs and the breeding range was still expanding. The north and west of the country supports the majority of pairs and the Red Kite is still scarce in central and eastern areas (Adamski 1995). A more recent population estimate suggests that, by the end of the 1990s, there were up to 700 pairs in the country (Pawel Brzek pers. comm.).

Slovakia

Poland's southern neighbour Slovakia, has seen a marked decrease in numbers during recent decades with the population in the early 1990s estimated at no more than 10-20 pairs (Tucker & Heath 1994, Snow & Perrins 1998).

Hungary

The Red Kite declined rapidly to near extinction in Hungary in the 1950s and 1960s, possibly as a result of poisoning by organochlorine pesticides used in agriculture (Bijleveld 1974). It was then mainly a rare visitor, with just an occasional breeding pair in the south of the country (Szabolcs Kókay pers. comm.). Breeding has now, once more, become regular with an estimated 4-10 pairs by the early 2000s (BirdLife International 2004).

Romania

In Romania an estimated 15-20 pairs were present in the mid-1990s (Snow & Perrins 1998) but, in recent years, the population is thought to have declined (BirdLife International 2004).

Macedonia, Croatia and Serbia & Montenegro (former Yuguslavia)

A long-term decline has taken place in the former Yugoslavia where the species was formerly widely distributed in the north and in Macedonia. A few pairs may still breed in Croatia and in Serbia & Montenegro (Snow & Perrins 1998, BirdLife International 2004).

Former Soviet Union

In the former Soviet Union only very limited information on status is available compared with most of the rest of Europe. The Baltic Republics of Latvia and Lithuania may each support a handful of pairs, while in Estonia the Red Kite is only an occasional visitor. Further south, in Belarus, the first confirmed breeding records since the 1950s occurred in 1985 and 1994 (Nikiforov 1996), and the population was estimated at 3-10 pairs in the mid-1990s (BirdLife International 2004). Ukraine may have supported up to 5-8 pairs in 1990 and neighbouring Moldova just a single pair in the same year but populations in both countries were thought to be extinct by 2000 (BirdLife International 2004). Only a few isolated pairs are thought to survive on the eastern seaboard of the Black Sea in Georgia, Russia and Azerbaijan. In the former USSR as a whole the total population is probably less than 100 pairs (Snow & Perrins 1998).

Iberia and the Balearic Islands

Spain

Spain was, until recently, second only to Germany in terms of the size of its breeding population but it now apparently supports fewer pairs than France following huge declines in many areas. In common with Germany there was considerable uncertainty as to the true population size in the past with estimates ranging from as little as 1,000 to as many as 10,000 pairs in the 1980s (Cramp & Simmons 1980, Meyburg & Meyburg 1987). During 1994, the first full national census, carried out using both road-transect counts and counts of breeding territories, gave an estimate of 3,328-4,044 pairs (Viñuela *et al*. 1999). The distribution was found to be patchy with some provinces in western and central Spain supporting densities as high as those commonly found in central Europe, but other areas with only low densities or no birds at all. The latest estimate is that only 2,000-2,200 breeding pairs remain following a decline approaching 50% across the country during the previous decade (BirdLife International 2004, Cardiel 2006). In the province of Segovia in central Spain, the population may have declined by as much as 80-90% in the ten years to 2003 (Javier Viñuela pers. comm.).

Viñuela *et al*. (1999) blamed the declines in Spain on the two main problems affecting Spanish raptors generally – persecution (particularly poisoning and shooting) and, to a far lesser extent, electrocution by power lines. Reductions in extensive livestock farming and competition with Black Kites might also have had adverse effects in some areas.

The Balearics

There have also been alarming declines in the numbers of Red Kites on the two Balearic Islands of Majorca and Minorca. In Majorca, the Red Kite was fairly common until the 1950s, before suffering a drastic reduction to only 27 pairs. In Minorca the situation is even worse. A population estimated at 135 pairs in the late 1980s crashed to only eight pairs by 1998. On both islands the declines have been attributed to poisoning and electrocution by powerlines (Viñuela *et al*. 1999). In order to try to address these problems recovery plans have been instigated in both islands involving research to clearly identify the main problems and a campaign of education to try to reduce illegal killing.

Portugal

The Red Kite is one of the most heavily persecuted raptors in Portugal and has declined markedly over recent decades. By the mid-1980s, the population was thought to be only 100-200 pairs (Rufino *et al*. 1985, Viñuela 1999) and the situation has deteriorated even further in recent years. Only 50-100 pairs are now thought to remain (BirdLife International 2004).

Central and eastern Mediterranean

Italy

A long-term decline in Italy appears to have been halted, and population estimates have increased from 110-140 pairs in the early 1990s (Viñuela 1996) to 300-400 pairs by 2003 (BirdLife International 2004). This may, in part, reflect the fact that more comprehensive survey work has been undertaken in recent years. Persecution, in the form of poisoning, and interference at nests remain serious problems in some areas. The islands of Sicily and Sardinia were formerly strongholds but numbers have fallen rapidly during the last 20 years. The decline has been particularly dramatic in Sicily where a population of 70-100 pairs has been reduced to only 12-14 pairs as a result of poisoning and nest interference (Snow & Perrins 1998).

Corsica

Corsica is the only one of the five major Mediterranean islands within the Red Kite's range where there has not been a steep decline in numbers. Patrimonio (1990) estimated the population at 100-180 pairs, despite the threat posed by the use of strychnine baits to control Red Foxes. By 2002, Thiollay and Bretagnolle (2004) suggested that the population had increased to 208-277 pairs, including an increase from 25-30 pairs to 70-90 pairs in a stronghold in the northwest of the island in less than ten years. Increases in Rabbit numbers since their introduction in the late 1970s have provided a major food source for Red Kites, and it is also believed that levels of human persecution may have declined (Mougeot 2000, Mougeot & Bretagnolle 2006).

Canary Islands

It is thought that the Red Kite became extinct on the islands in the late 1960s or early 1970s and the species is now only an irregular and uncommon visitor (Blanco & González 1992, Snow & Perrins 1998). Ferguson-Lees and Christie (2001) suggested that pesticide campaigns against locusts may have been the cause of extinction.

Cape Verde Islands

There has been much confusion regarding the status of the Cape Verde Kite. The predominant view until recently was that this bird represents a distinct subspecies of the Red Kite, *Milvus milvus fasciicauda*, with characteristics intermediate between those of Black Kite and the European race of Red Kite. However, recent genetic work has cast some doubt on this (see Chapter 1). This form was still reported to be widespread in the islands up until the 1950s but, by the early 1990s, only small numbers were thought to remain on the islands of Santiago and Santo Antão. Snow and Perrins (1998) suggested that there were up to 50-75 pairs although it is likely that this estimate was far too high due to confusion with Black Kites. A study by Hille (1998) in 1996-97 found only 5-6 individuals thought to be of this form, all on the western-most island of Santo Antão, and there was no evidence of breeding. Black Kite numbers had also declined dramatically. Reasons put forward to explain these alarming declines include human persecution, an increase in aridity on the islands, pressure from human activities, and overgrazing by livestock. Ferguson-Lees and Christie (2001) suggested that poisoning campaigns against feral cats and dogs, and the subsequent dumping of the contaminated carcasses in the open countryside may have played a role in the decline. In 2002, a full search of the islands located only five prospective Cape Verde Kites all of which were taken into captivity as part of a conservation programme (Johnson *et al.* 2005). Analysis of blood samples from these birds showed that all, in fact, contained Black Kite DNA appearing to confirm that the Cape Verde Kite no longer survives.

North Africa and the Middle East

The Red Kite is now very scarce in North Africa and there has been no recent proof of breeding. The largest population in recent times was in Morocco where 10-100 pairs were thought to occur in the early 1980s (Snow & Perrins 1998). There has since been a marked decline with no proven records in recent years. However, the main breeding areas in the Rif and Middle Atlas mountains in northern Morocco are not well monitored and it is possible that a small breeding population remains. Algeria and Tunisia formerly supported small breeding populations but Red Kites are now only seen in low numbers during the winter. It is thought that very small numbers may breed in Turkey, Iran and Iraq but there have been no confirmed breeding records from these countries in recent times.

Overall population and status

In the 1980s, the Red Kite was considered by the World Conservation Union (IUCN) to be Globally Threatened, meaning that unless appropriate action was taken, there was a danger that the species would continue to decline towards extinction (Collar & Andrew 1988). The only other British species at the time with the same categorisation were White-tailed Sea Eagle and Corncrake. There was considerable uncertainty as to the overall Red Kite population with Collar and Andrew (1988) suggesting that it was between 5,500 and 15,000 pairs, and a review by Evans and Pienkowski (1991) providing a somewhat narrower estimate of 11,000-13,000 pairs. Increases in some areas of northwest and central Europe, and an upward revision of the population estimate for Germany, the most important country, led to much higher estimates in the 1990s. Tucker and Heath (1994) thought that there were between 19,000 and 37,000 pairs, with the large range reflecting the lack of an accurate population estimate for some countries, including Germany. As a result of these higher estimates, the Red Kite was downgraded to Least Concern in the IUCN Red List although it remained a Species of European Conservation Concern due to its restricted range in Europe (Tucker & Heath 1994).

In the last 15 years or so, better information has become available on population size and trends in many European countries. Fortunes have varied dramatically with large increases in some countries, including Sweden, Switzerland, Poland and Britain, but worrying declines in other parts of the range. Declines in Germany, France and Spain are of particular concern as these countries support by far the largest breeding populations. BirdLife International (2004) concluded that, overall, there had been a decline of greater than 10% in the period 1990-2000. In response, the IUCN revised the Red Kite's threat status to Near Threatened in 2005 on the basis that it is close, once again, to meeting the criteria for being Globally Threatened.

The review carried out for the first edition of this book in 2001 put the world population at 18-24,000 pairs and suggested that the overall trend in numbers was now roughly stable, with recent increases in some countries balancing declines in others. The BirdLife International (2004) review estimated the population at 19-25,000 pairs, providing further evidence that the population has indeed now stabilised. Even so, large parts of the Red Kite's historical range have yet to be recolonised and other areas support far lower densities than was the case in the past. Worrying declines continue in some areas and the total population remains well below the level that might be expected were it not for the adverse effects of persecution during the last two centuries.

The world Red Kite population is put into perspective by considering the similar sized Common Buzzard. Clements (2002) estimated that, despite the continued absence of this species from much suitable habitat in central and eastern parts of the country, there were 44-61,000 territorial pairs of Buzzards in Britain. The lower end of this estimate is approximately twice as high as the total world Red Kite population. The European Buzzard population (including Russia) was estimated in Hagemeijer and Blair (1997) as 903,000 pairs, making it approximately 45 times more numerous than the Red Kite.

Chapter 4

MIGRATION AND
WINTERING AREAS

The Red Kite shows considerable variation in migratory behaviour in different parts of its range. Some populations are largely resident and, once an individual has bred for the first time, it may not stray further than a few kilometres from its nest site for the rest of its life. By contrast, the majority of Red Kites in other populations undertake a prolonged migration between separate breeding and wintering areas each year, amounting to tens of thousands of kilometres during the course of an average life. Displaced migrants are regular in parts of Europe close to the main breeding or wintering areas and there is a small, but regular, spring passage through coastal counties of southern and eastern Britain, made up largely of continental birds.

Reasons for migration

It is in northern, central and eastern Europe, where winters are harsher than in western and southern Europe, that the Red Kite is primarily a migratory species. In these areas, the majority of the population undertakes an annual return journey of 3,000km or more to spend the winter in more temperate climes, mainly in Spain. In Britain, the moderating influence of the maritime climate means that winters are far less severe, and here, as in southern Europe, Red Kites are mainly resident.

There are clearly costs involved in undertaking a long distance migration and, for it to be worthwhile, these must be outweighed by the benefits of wintering in an area with a more temperate climate or more abundant food supply. Survival during a harsh winter is certainly more difficult than in areas where conditions are less severe. For one thing, more food must be consumed in cold conditions simply in order to maintain body temperature. Moreover, food may be harder to come by, as many potential prey species migrate south in order to escape the conditions. Prolonged snow cover is particularly difficult for a species that is so heavily dependent on animal carrion. Once carcasses are covered with snow, they become inaccessible to the Red Kite with its reliance on keen eyesight to locate food.

Distribution in winter

Iberia supports the bulk of the world Red Kite population in winter, including most of the large, central European breeding population. There are no good estimates for the numbers present in Portugal but they are thought to be relatively low and Spain undoubtedly supports the majority of the population. A census was carried out in Spain in the winter of 1993/94 using a combination of road transect surveys and counts of birds at communal roost sites (Viñuela et al. 1999). This estimated the total number of wintering birds at 66,000-70,000. Taking into account the resident Spanish population, approximately 54,000-62,000 of these birds were thought to have originated from breeding areas in central and northern Europe. A more recent survey in 2004 estimated the wintering population at only 29,000-30,000 birds, excluding birds from the sedentary Spanish population (Cardiel 2006). The distribution of birds is patchy with the southern slopes of the Pyrenees, and parts of Castilla y León, on the northern plateau, found to be particularly important. Densities vary from 2 birds/km^2 in limited areas to

0-0.5/km^2 across the majority of the range. Some lowland areas of Spain without any breeding birds, support significant numbers of Red Kites in winter, and it has been suggested that the lack of competition from the migratory Black Kite at this time of year may make such areas more attractive. On a more local scale, the highest densities were found in areas with an abundance of poultry and livestock carrion, an important source of food for wintering Red Kites in Spain. Although some Spanish breeding pairs are sedentary, remaining close to their nest sites throughout the year, others undertake movements within Spain, often mixing with immigrants from central Europe.

Far smaller numbers winter elsewhere in southern Europe. Sagot (1991) estimated that the wintering population in southwest France, close to the western Pyrenees, was around 1,000-1,500 individuals, with lower numbers elsewhere in the country. In Italy, surveys carried out in 1997/98 and 1998/99 recorded 850-1,150 wintering birds, mainly concentrated in central-southern Italy, and it was estimated that the total population was up to 1,500 birds (Corso *et al.* 1999). Communal roosts in southern Italy can hold up to 200 birds (Gaibani *et al.* 2001).

Only very low numbers of Red Kites are believed to over-winter in North Africa. Counts at Gibraltar, the main crossing point between south-western Europe and North Africa for many migratory birds of prey, have included up to 200 Red Kites during the spring and autumn migration periods (Bergier 1987). A handful of birds have been recorded in some years at other well-known raptor migration bottlenecks further east in the Mediterranean, including the Bosphorus in Turkey and Cap Bon in Tunisia, suggesting that at least small numbers may winter in these, and adjacent, countries (Urcun & Bried 1998).

As expected, the majority of recoveries of Red Kites ringed in central Europe have been from Spain, southern Portugal and southern France. There have also been recoveries from Italy, Sardinia and the Balkans (Cramp & Simmons 1980), confirming that some of the birds wintering in central or eastern parts of the Mediterranean are from the central European breeding population.

Changes in wintering range

Since the late 1950s there has been an increasing tendency for a proportion of birds from northern and central European populations to remain in their breeding areas during the winter (Ulfstrand 1963, Hagemeijer & Blair 1997). A census in 1991 located approximately 500 birds wintering in Sweden, including a single roost of 200 birds. Most of the wintering birds are adults and this is reflected in records of birds migrating south at the Falsterbo watch point at the southern tip of Sweden. In the autumns of 1987-1990, adults made up just 16% of the total of 1,507 birds recorded migrating south (Kjellén 1994). It is not surprising that a higher proportion of adult birds remain in the breeding areas in winter as they are already familiar with the local landscape and its food supply, and they may risk their breeding site being usurped if they leave the area (Newton 1979). Immature birds have less attachment to the breeding areas and many opt to take advantage of more favourable conditions well to the south in winter.

In central Europe, overwintering was considered exceptional until the early 1960s but has since become a regular occurrence with substantial numbers attending communal roosts in some areas. One of the largest roosts in eastern Germany held up to 250 birds in November 1994 (George 1995). In Switzerland, wintering was first reported in 1969/70 and has now become regular, with a total population of at least 400-600 birds at two large, and a number of smaller, roosts (Mosimann & Juillard 1988, Müller 1995). There is little information on the age composition of groups of Red Kites overwintering in central Europe, although both adults and young of the year are known to be present at communal roosts in Germany.

The reason for this change in wintering behaviour is not fully clear. Juillard (1977) suggested that an increase in refuse tips and the resulting increase in food availability was a likely factor in the increased wintering numbers in central Europe. In Sweden it has also been suggested that increased food supply in winter, this time as a result of a programme of winter feeding, may have increased the wintering population. However, when the official feeding programme ceased in 1990/91 this did not result in a reduction in wintering numbers (Kjellén 1995). Improvements in waste-disposal methods in Germany were believed to have led to local reductions in wintering numbers there as a result of reduced food availability (Alistair Hill in litt., quoted by Evans & Pienkowski 1991) although this does not appear to have led to a long term reduction in the country as a whole. Milder winters (on average) over the last few decades may well be a significant factor (Snow & Perrins 1998). It is interesting that some Black Kites now remain for the winter in Spain rather than undertaking their usual migration to south of the Sahara (Muntaner & Mayol 1996). If, in coming years, global warming results in a reduction in the severity of winters across central and northern Europe, then a higher proportion of the Red Kite population may forgo the annual migration.

Viñuela et al. (1999) thought that short-term changes in weather patterns in central Europe were an important factor in determining how many birds remained in the breeding areas each winter. They noted the considerable inter-annual variation in the number of Red Kites wintering in Spain and suggested that, in harsh winters, a higher proportion of the population was likely to migrate south from central and northern Europe.

Migratory behaviour and timing

Some Red Kites begin to move south towards their wintering areas in late summer as shown by the recovery of a German-ringed bird in southwest France in late August (Cramp & Simmons 1980). Movements begin in earnest, however, in September, and passage through France is at its highest during the second half of September and through October. A long-term study of the autumn migration of Red Kites through the Pyrenees (Urcun & Bried 1998) found that passage was concentrated at several south-facing mountain valleys, particularly at the western end of the range. Between 5,000 and 10,000 birds were recorded in most years with the bulk of the movements in the last week of September and during October, later than the main passage of most other birds of prey through the area. Movements continued into November although, by this time, most birds are already settled in their wintering areas. Figure 3 shows the clear difference in the migration periods of Black and Red Kites in the Pyrenees. Black Kites begin to cross south in mid-July and the bulk of the movements are during August. By the end of August only very small numbers are still passing through, well before the start of the main passage of Red Kites. Black Kites have by far the longer migration of the two species as they winter in Africa south of the Sahara desert. They are also less tolerant of cool and damp conditions than Red Kites and both these factors favour a southwards movement as early as possible after the breeding season. In contrast, Red Kites have only a relatively short onward journey into Spain to their wintering areas and seem better adapted to cope with the cool and damp conditions that are sometimes found in central Europe in late summer. In spring, Black Kites arrive back in their breeding areas, on average, several weeks later than Red Kites and so must compress their breeding season into a much shorter period (Snow & Perrins 1998).

As is to be expected from the more northerly location, Red Kites move through Falsterbo in southern Sweden rather earlier in the autumn. The passage starts in August and continues through September and into October in some years. The median date for juvenile birds in 1986-1990 was 26 September, around two weeks earlier than the equivalent date in the Pyrenees. Kjellén (1992) noted that the Red Kite was highly dependent on thermals and in some years the majority of birds could pass through in just a few days when weather conditions were suitable. At Falsterbo, the more numerous juveniles tend to move through a few days earlier, on average, than the adult birds (Kjellén 1992). The minority of birds that remain in central Europe for the winter may undertake a southwards

Figure 3: **Timing of autumn migration of Red and Black Kites across the Pyrenees, 1981-94** *(from Urcun & Bried 1998)*

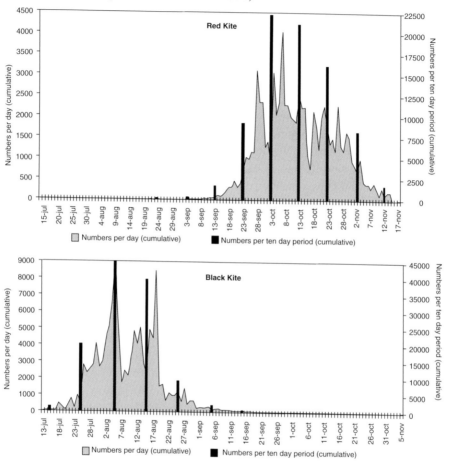

movement at almost any time if there is a sustained spell of poor weather, apparently even as late as February, not long before the usual onset of return migration (George 1994).

Most Red Kites arrive back in their breeding areas during March, with northwards movements beginning in about mid-February and continuing into April and May in northern Europe. Gottschalk (1995) found that birds passing through the Vortaunus region of western Germany between 1984 and 1994 were concentrated into a relatively short period from the last week of February until about mid-March, with only low numbers of passage birds in April and May.

It is believed that the males generally return to their breeding sites before the females, as is often the case in migratory species, although the difficulty in sexing birds in the field means that there is no hard evidence to confirm this.

Migrant Red Kites in spring tend to be less gregarious than is the case in autumn. In Gottschalk's (1995) study, singles and small groups of up to 10-15 birds predominated in spring, whereas in autumn, groups of between 30 and 50 birds were relatively common. Urcun and Bried (1998) recorded flocks of up to 100 birds passing through the Pyrenees in autumn, although the average group size during the peak migration period was only 3-4 birds. There may be greater opportunity for flocking during the more leisurely autumn migration with birds gathering together in the same areas whilst awaiting suitable conditions for onward migration. In spring, the adults are no doubt keen to return to their breeding areas and re-establish territories as quickly as possible, and are therefore perhaps more willing to continue travelling in adverse conditions.

It is not thought that birds travel in family parties during the autumn migration but juveniles may well benefit from migrating in groups with more experienced adult birds. Adults will have already successfully completed at least one migration to and from the wintering areas in southern Europe whereas juveniles will be undertaking the journey for the first time. This is perhaps another reason why flocking tends to be more common during the autumn migration.

In recent years, Red Kites in Germany and Switzerland have been fitted with satellite tags allowing them to be tracked remotely by satellite receivers. Already this work has provided useful insights into migratory behaviour as well as some rather unexpected patterns of movements. The relatively leisurely nature of the autumn migration has been confirmed. For example, one tagged youngster began to head southwest from Switzerland in the last week in September, then spent almost three weeks from 3-21 October on the northern slopes of the Pyrenees in southern France, before finally crossing into northern Spain, sometime during the period 21-27 October. It did not reach its final wintering destination in Castilla y León, northern Spain, until the end of October, more than a month after its journey had begun. Another young bird fitted with a satellite tag in Switzerland in 2004, migrated southwest to winter in Haute-Garonne, southern France, in the autumn, about 600km from its breeding site. In April 2005 it made the return journey to Switzerland as expected but, only ten days later, it moved back to its wintering site in France. Two weeks later it was back in Switzerland where it spent the summer before returning to its wintering site in southern France in the autumn. In spring 2006 it exhibited similar behaviour, moving back to Switzerland in February, only to return to France a few days later (Adrian Aebischer pers. comm.). It is not clear what benefits such repeated, long distance, movements bring but there is a clear similarity here with the dispersive, presumably exploratory, movements made by young Red Kites in non-migratory populations, something considered in more detail in Chapter 10.

It is known from ringing recoveries that some immature birds from central European breeding grounds remain in the Spanish wintering areas throughout their second calendar year (Cramp & Simmons 1980). These individuals presumably delay the long journey back to the natal area until they are old enough to breed, usually when they are at least two years old.

Displaced migrants

In Britain, Red Kite records away from the main breeding areas involve a combination of migrants from central and northern Europe, and young birds dispersing from the Welsh and, since 1989, reintroduced, populations in England and Scotland (see Chapter 10). Records are most numerous in southern and, particularly, eastern coastal counties and the pattern of records, with a clear peak in early spring, suggests that the majority of these birds are displaced migrants on route between wintering areas in Iberia and breeding sites in central or northern Europe (see below). Autumn and winter records are more likely to involve wandering juveniles from within Britain but no doubt also include a small proportion of continental birds. The general pattern of occurrence is shown for various counties in Table 4. The spring peak is obvious, with records in March and April accounting for 39% of the annual total. Relatively few birds are seen during the summer months and records then increase again in autumn and winter.

It is interesting to note that the spring peak of records in English counties was noticeably earlier before the reintroduction programme began in Britain in 1989 (Table 4). For the pre-1989 period, a total of 29% of records were in March, with 28% of birds recorded in April and May combined. March records in the post-1989 period involve only 20% of the total birds seen in the year, easily exceeded by the 29% of birds recorded during April and May combined. Studies of marked individuals in England have confirmed that most birds dispersing from the resident, reintroduced, populations in spring do so in April or May (Dixon 2001, Carter & Grice 2002). The March peak in Table 4 is therefore strongly indicative of a spring passage of continental birds, with the higher proportion of birds recorded later in the spring, post-1989, reflecting increasing numbers of dispersing birds from the reintroduced population.

In 1996 there was a particularly impressive spring passage of birds along the English east coast. This was most apparent in Norfolk where the first bird was seen on 9 March and, from then until 1 June, an estimated 45 birds were recorded, two more than were seen in the county throughout the whole of the 1980s (Taylor *et al*. 1999). It is unlikely that many were wandering birds from the reintroduction programme as none were reported to have wing-tags. In stark contrast to this glut of spring records, a mere two birds were reported in Norfolk during the following autumn.

The majority of passage birds in Britain are likely to be on route to breeding areas in central or northern Europe. Some evidence for this is provided by a small number of records of individually-marked birds that have been recovered

Table 4: **Monthly totals[1] of Red Kites in English counties away from breeding areas before and after the start of the reintroduction programme**
(from Brown & Grice 2005)

County	Jan	Feb	Mar	Apr	May	Jun	Jul	Aug	Sep	Oct	Nov	Dec
Pre-1989												
Sussex 1960-1988	4	2	10	6	5	3	0	1	1	3	8	4
Essex 1960-1988	4	2	6	17	1	1	0	0	0	0	4	4
Norfolk 1970-1988	5	3	40	16	7	2	1	1	1	0	4	15
Northumberland 1970-1988	0	1	1	3	0	0	0	0	0	1	1	1
Cumbria 1970-1988	0	0	3	1	1	1	2	1	0	1	0	2
Dorset 1950-1988	1	2	5	5	2	1	0	1	1	2	2	4
Total	**14**	**10**	**65**	**48**	**16**	**8**	**3**	**4**	**3**	**7**	**19**	**30**
Post-1989												
Sussex 1989-2000	5	5	19	16	19	6	2	5	3	6	7	5
Essex 1989-2000	3	1	9	7	1	2	9	3	3	6	3	2
Norfolk 1989-2000	12	18	73	53	43	20	24	14	8	11	8	20
Northumberland 1989-2000	0	1	2	7	0	1	0	1	0	2	2	2
Cumbria 1989-2000	3	1	2	3	0	2	0	0	0	2	0	1
Cornwall 1989-2000	5	3	10	6	9	6	2	1	7	8	9	3
Dorset 1989-2000	12	4	15	10	15	12	0	3	0	12	10	4
Total	**40**	**33**	**130**	**102**	**89**	**49**	**37**	**27**	**21**	**47**	**39**	**37**

[1] Figures may include some duplicate records where an individual bird has been seen at two or more locations

in Britain, including at least six German-ringed birds (Toms & Clark 1998). These include an individual fledged in Schleswig-Holstein in June 1971 that was found dead at Pantydwr near Rhayader in July 1972, probably as a result of poisoning (Walters Davies & Davis 1973), and a bird ringed in Sachsen that was found in Essex about one year after it had fledged.

There is a similar pattern of records on the near continent where there is also a regular spring passage of Red Kites, particularly in areas adjacent to significant breeding populations. The Netherlands, for example, does not support a breeding population but is close to the large population in Germany. The main passage through The Netherlands is from mid-February to mid-May and this period accounts for, on average, 63% of records each year (SOVON 1987). The majority of the birds seen early in the spring are adults, presumably keen to return to their breeding sites at the earliest opportunity. In April and May an increasing proportion of the birds are non-breeding immatures. These birds have no breeding site to hurry back to and can therefore afford a more leisurely migration. A few non-breeding birds remain in the country throughout the summer and there is a slight increase in birds seen in the autumn, although involving far lower numbers than in spring.

For many scarce migrants, autumn records usually outnumber those in spring, reflecting the larger population sizes following the breeding season and also the fact that juveniles are less experienced than adults and are more prone to stray from the usual migration route. The relative lack of passage Red Kites in autumn in Britain and the near continent is probably a result of birds from the largest breeding populations in central Europe heading south or southwest towards wintering areas at this time. Only a large discrepancy from the usual direction of migration would take birds towards northwest Europe and Britain. By contrast, in spring when birds are heading back north from Iberia towards the breeding grounds, only a relatively minor deviation from the usual migration direction can result in birds arriving in adjacent countries to the west of the breeding areas, including Britain. It is also possible that different migration routes may be involved in spring and autumn, as in many other migrant species, and this may be a contributory factor explaining the higher number of arrivals in Britain in spring.

Vagrants

As a result of the Red Kite's migratory habits in parts of its range and the tendency for some first-year birds to disperse even in resident populations, vagrants have been reported from many countries outside the usual range. Snow and Perrins (1998) listed Finland, Malta, Armenia, Cyprus, Lebanon, Israel,

Libya and Madeira as countries where the Red Kite was a rare visitor. Ferguson-Lees and Christie (2001) added Syria, Jordan, Saudi Arabia and Egypt, whilst cautioning that confusion with rufous examples of immature, eastern-race, Black Kites could be obscuring the true picture. In North Africa and parts of the Middle East, there is also the potential for confusion between Long-legged Buzzard and Red Kite due to similarities in size and colour between the two species. Ferguson-Lees and Christie (2001) were highly sceptical of records of Red Kites from even further afield including four apparent observations in India since 1945, one supposedly involving 'over 50 . . . . assembled for scraps around a shooting camp in lightly wooded semi-desert' (Ali & Riply 1978). Vagrant Red Kites have also been reported from Bangladesh (Sarker & Sarker 1985), Nepal (Inskipp & Inskipp 1991), The Gambia (Geeson & Geeson 1990), and from both East and South Africa, the latter again being viewed with some scepticism by Ferguson-Lees and Christie (2001). There have been at least six records from the Channel Islands (Davies 2002) and Iceland has recently seen its first record following the arrival of a first-year bird originating from northern Scotland (see Chapter 10).

Chapter 5

REINTRODUCTION

During the past few decades many different birds of prey have been the subject of reintroduction attempts in a large number of countries across the world. Much of the early work was carried out in the United States where projects to restore populations of Peregrine, Osprey and the highly endangered California Condor commenced in the 1970s and 1980s. In Britain, the first efforts to reintroduce the White-tailed Sea Eagle in Scotland were made as early as 1959, although a breeding population has only become established as a result of further releases from 1975 to 1998.

Birds of prey feature disproportionately highly in reintroduction projects for a number of reasons, connected both to their ecology and to human attitudes towards them. As they are often at the top of the food chain, and occur at relatively low densities, they are especially vulnerable to the adverse effects of human activities, including habitat destruction, pesticide poisoning and direct persecution. This has resulted in the complete loss of some species from large parts of their range. Even if conditions improve, natural recolonisation may be hindered by a slow reproductive rate and the inbuilt tendency for the individuals of many species to breed close to the area where they themselves were born and reared (see Chapter 10). The young of most birds of prey are relatively easy to rear in captivity, at least for a short period, and they require only daily provisioning with food. In contrast, projects involving small passerines may require complex captive-rearing techniques in order to rear young successfully, including food provisioning many times each day.

Birds of prey are generally popular with the public as a result of their impressive size or spectacular hunting behaviour. As a result conservation organisations often find it easier to attract funds for projects involving such high profile species than is the case with other, possibly equally deserving, groups. Work to restore populations of birds of prey encourages changes to the environment that benefit a wide range of other wildlife. If conditions are suitable for the reintroduction of a top predator then there must be adequate populations of prey species as well as sufficient suitable habitat for breeding and finding food. The factors that caused the loss of the species in the first place must also have been addressed. This could involve educational campaigns to tackle problems of persecution or pesticide poisoning, or a programme of habitat management, all resulting in benefits to a wide range of different species.

This chapter concentrates on work to reintroduce the Red Kite to England and Scotland, describing the background to the reintroduction programme, the methods used and the progress that has been achieved since the first birds were released into the wild in 1989. Table 7, at the end of the chapter, provides summary details for other recent projects in Europe involving the reintroduction of birds of prey.

Background to reintroduction in England and Scotland

In the mid-1980s the Red Kite was one of only three species in Britain considered by the World Conservation Union (IUCN) to be threatened on a global scale, and, as such, was a particularly high priority for conservation. Although the small population in central Wales was recovering from past persecution, the rate of recovery was very slow as a result of the cool, damp climate and unproductive habitat. In 1986, the Nature Conservancy Council (now Natural England in England and Scottish Natural Heritage in Scotland) and the RSPB set up a Red Kite Project Team to look at ways in which the fortunes of the species could be improved. After careful consideration, it was agreed that, as well as continued conservation efforts in Wales, an experimental project should be undertaken to evaluate reintroduction as a method for restoring Red Kites to suitable areas throughout England and Scotland. At this stage not everyone was convinced that the project would be a success. Some senior figures in the ornithological world found it hard to believe that the Red Kite would do well in our modern lowland landscapes such a long time after it had been driven to extinction, and expressed serious reservations about the project going ahead.

Reintroduction is not an option that should be undertaken lightly. It requires a long-term commitment, with sufficient funding to carry out the necessary releases of birds, often over many years, and for a programme of monitoring to detect any problems at an early stage. Internationally agreed guidelines for reintroduction projects have been established by the World Conservation Union (Green 1979, updated by IUCN (1995)), and the experimental Red Kite project was only given the go ahead once it was clear that it complied with these in full. The following summary, based on the IUCN criteria, demonstrates that the Red Kite was a suitable candidate for reintroduction (see Carter *et al*. 1995 and Evans *et al*. 1997 for more details).

• Historical evidence of former natural occurrence

Projects involving translocation should normally only seek to restore species that are a natural part of the area's wildlife. In the case of the Red Kite there was good evidence from old avifaunas and other literature that the species was formerly widespread and, in places, very common in England and Scotland.

• A clear understanding of the factors causing extinction (and these factors should no longer apply)

The Red Kite became extinct in England and Scotland as a direct result of intensive human persecution. Birds of prey are still persecuted in parts of Britain today, but levels of persecution have reduced due to changes in public attitudes and improved legislation. It was thought unlikely that a species harmless to farming and game-rearing interests would be persecuted to such a degree that the reintroduction project would be jeopardised.

● **Suitable habitat available to support the reintroduced population**

Although the countryside has changed dramatically during the 200 years since it was last a familiar sight across Britain, studies of the Red Kite's ecology in Wales and elsewhere in Europe indicated that the majority of the former range in England and Scotland was still suitable. In fact, the patchwork of mixed farmland and woodland that is typical of large areas of lowland Britain was thought to provide ideal nesting, roosting and foraging habitats.

● **A suitable source of birds for release (without jeopardising the donor population)**

At the start of the project there were two main options for obtaining Red Kites for release. The birds could either be bred in captivity or taken from donor populations in the wild. Captive breeding was tried using injured adult birds from Spain that were unfit for release back into the wild. This proved to be very difficult and it quickly became clear that, in order to obtain sufficient birds for a large-scale release programme, it would be necessary to take birds from a donor population. Red Kites are still common in parts of continental Europe and the authorities in several areas with healthy populations agreed to supply young birds for the programme.

One factor not mentioned in the IUCN guidelines – but referred to in the Joint Nature Conservation Committee's recent translocations policy (JNCC 2003) – is the potential for natural recolonisation. It is common sense that if a species is able to recolonise an area naturally within a reasonable period of time then there is no need for a time consuming and expensive reintroduction project, and the resources should be used for a more deserving cause. The Welsh Red Kite population had long been hampered in its recovery by the unsuitable climate and unproductive (in terms of foraging) countryside, and there were also concerns that the use of poison baits to control corvids and Foxes in the border counties of England and Wales might be hindering population expansion. Between 1971 and 1989, a minimum of 28 Red Kites were killed by poison, ten of which were birds found dead in England (Cadbury 1991, Evans *et al.* 1997). Despite many years of protection and dedicated conservation efforts, in the late 1980s there were no signs of the range extending from Wales into more suitable lowland areas in central and eastern Britain.

Reintroduction methods

The first phase of the reintroduction programme was carried out over five years at two sites, one in southern England and a second in northern Scotland. These release projects, beginning in 1989, were initially regarded as experimental, the main aim being to establish and test methods by which Red Kites could be re-established in the wild. If the initial projects proved to be successful then they could be repeated elsewhere in order to restore the species to suitable areas throughout Britain.

Selection of the first two release areas

The majority of lowland Britain is suitable for the Red Kite with its undemanding habitat requirements and generalist diet. Only in urban areas and perhaps in areas of countryside with few trees, such as the East Anglian fens, would Red Kites probably struggle to survive. It was nevertheless felt to be important that the first two reintroduction attempts were carried out in areas that offered conditions as close as possible to ideal in order to maximise the survival rates of released birds and improve the chances that breeding populations would become established.

The Project Team set out a series of simple criteria for selecting potential areas, based on knowledge of the Red Kite's main requirements and causes of mortality in its existing range (Lovegrove *et al*. 1990):

1. There should be a sufficiently large area of suitable habitat and not an isolated patch of good habitat in an otherwise unsuitable landscape. Good habitat comprises a combination of woodland for nesting and roosting, and mixed farmland, including both grassland and arable crops, to provide foraging areas.

2. The area should support a sustainable food supply in both summer and winter.

3. The breeding success of Buzzards (if present) should be high, indicating a good food supply and a low level of persecution.

4. So far as possible, the area should be known to be free from illegal poison baits.

5. The area should have a low annual rainfall and be below an altitude of 350m above sea level.

6. The local community in the area should be supportive of the project.

The two areas finally selected were the Chiltern Hills on the Oxfordshire/Buckinghamshire border in the south of England and the Black Isle in northern Scotland. In both areas a number of landowners were contacted and asked if they would agree to support the project by allowing birds to be released on their estates. Several estates agreed to host the projects and preparations began in earnest during 1989 with the construction of large wooden release aviaries in both areas, ready to receive the first young birds later in the year. The following sections describe the methods used to re-establish the Red Kite in Britain; methods that were pioneered during the first phase of the reintroduction programme – see Evans *et al*. (1997) for further details. Following the successful establishment of self-sustaining breeding populations at both of the first two sites, releases have subsequently been carried out at a further six sites in Britain, three each in England and Scotland (see Table 6).

Collection of young

One potential option for collecting young Red Kites was to make use of the nest manipulation programme in Wales (see Chapter 11), with some of the young reared in captivity from 'rescued' eggs or chicks being used for the reintroduction programme rather than returned to nests in Wales. Initially, this seemed to be the most obvious source of birds, making full use of the surviving native Red Kite population and utilising rearing techniques that had been tested and shown to be effective. But there were a number of problems. One concern was that studies of the genetics of the Welsh population revealed a very low level of genetic variation, the result of inbreeding when the population was reduced to only a handful of birds in the 1930s (May *et al*. 1993b). It was thought that inbreeding might be a major factor in the poor productivity exhibited by the Welsh birds. Whatever the truth of this (and it now appears less likely based on improved breeding success in recent years) it seemed sensible to try to find a source of birds with more genetic variation. Indeed, it was argued that birds from more diverse continental populations were likely to be genetically closer to the birds that would have been present in England and Scotland a few hundred years previously, than were birds from the Welsh population. Continental birds and British birds would, after all, once have been part of the same, continuous, European population before this became fragmented as a result of human persecution (Evans *et al*. 1997).

A further problem in taking birds from Wales was the difficultly in being able to secure a sufficiently high number of individuals over a period of several years to supply two release projects, given that the Welsh population was still relatively small and vulnerable. It was true that the birds in the manipulation programme were derived from 'rescued' eggs that had either been deserted or were from nests at high risk from egg collectors. This would certainly have reduced any impact on the Welsh population. But such rescued birds had previously been returned to nests in the wild to contribute to the recovery of the Welsh population and many involved in the long-running protection programme in Wales understandably wanted to see this continue. In the end, a small number of Welsh young were donated to the reintroduction programme in the early years but, for the main source of birds, it was necessary to look further afield.

Thankfully, the authorities in several areas of mainland Europe supporting healthy populations of Red Kites agreed to take part in the reintroduction programme and offered to supply young birds for release in Britain. Most of the birds released in southern England were taken from northern Spain, while those released in northern Scotland were taken mainly from southern Sweden. Subsequent release projects have utilised birds taken from central Spain and Germany and, increasingly, birds are taken from populations already established by earlier releases in England and Scotland (Table 6)

Young are taken from nests when approximately 4-6 weeks old, a few weeks before they are old enough to make their first flight. Nests from which chicks are taken are always left with at least one nestling so that the adult pair remains at the site with a good chance of breeding successfully. It was believed that the chick or chicks left in donor nests stood a higher chance of survival once one or more of their siblings, and potential competitors for food, had been removed (Carter *et al*. 1999). However, recent evidence from collecting young in southern England has cast some doubt on this assumption because re-sighting rates for wing-tagged chicks left in donor nests appear to be lower than for those in nests that are not manipulated (Peter Stevens in litt.). The difference is small and based on only a small sample size so further work is required before this can be confirmed. The reason why chicks in donor nests may fare less well than chicks in other nests is unclear. Observations show that the donor nests are not abandoned by the adult birds, which continue to bring in food and attend to the young. Perhaps the remaining chick(s) interpret the disappearance of their siblings as predation and, fearing the same fate, try to leave the nest as soon as possible, sometimes before they are able to fly strongly. This could increase the risk of accidents and fledglings that end up on the ground due to poor flying ability become vulnerable to ground predators such as Foxes.

By the time that Red Kite nestlings reach four weeks of age, they are fully feathered and are able to regulate their own body temperature. They no longer require brooding by one of the parent birds during cool or wet weather, and so there is no need to provide an artificial heat source when they are held in captivity as would be necessary with younger, downy chicks. Collecting chicks when they are several weeks old also reduces the chance that they will become conditioned to humans during their time in captivity. Younger chicks need to be hand fed as, in the wild, they would be fed on small pieces of food offered by the parent birds. By four weeks, chicks are better able to handle food without assistance, and so hand feeding can be avoided. As a result the young stand a far better chance of adapting to life in the wild when they are released.

The Royal Air Force provided the transport for the birds flown to northern Scotland from Sweden. Birds from Spain and Germany were flown back on normal commercial flights with the birds travelling in small, hand-carried crates, within the aircraft's cargo hold. Because the Red Kite is listed on Annex A of regulations relating to the Convention on International Trade in Endangered Species (CITES), a licence had to be obtained before they could be imported to Britain. Separate licences were required from the donor countries in order to take the young from nests in the wild and, finally, an import licence from the British government was needed to allow the birds to be brought into the country. The amount of paperwork involved in an international project of this nature in modern times is not to be underestimated.

Ian Evans climbing to a nest in central Spain to collect nestlings for the reintroduction programme – in this case for release in Northamptonshire, central England (Ian Carter)

Care in captivity

The young Red Kites spend between 4-8 weeks in captivity, remaining in the aviary at the release site throughout this period. When they first arrive, the chicks are placed, three or four together, on an artificial stick nest in a covered section of the aviary. Food is provided daily on the nest using a small hatch built into each aviary compartment, so that the birds are not able to see humans when they are fed. Human contact is kept to an absolute minimum throughout the period of captivity and is limited to veterinary assessments and handling to fit wing-tags and radio-transmitters. Tiny holes in the wooden sides of the aviary compartments allow birds to be inspected without being aware of the presence of humans. Finding suitable sources of food is relatively easy as a result of the Red Kite's preference for carrion and its remarkably varied natural diet. Local farmers, gamekeepers and foresters provided food at some sites in the form of Muntjac, Fallow Deer, Rabbits, Grey Squirrels and corvids, controlled as part of their routine pest management programmes.

Each compartment within this release aviary in central England measures 8x8x20 feet, giving the birds room to exercise and strengthen their flight muscles. Plywood panels are used for the sides of the compartments with plastic mesh for the roof – see also the photograph on page 93 (Ian Carter)

Ian Evans and Karl Ivens with young Red Kites from Spain at the release aviary in central England (Ian Carter)

To provide variation, road casualty birds and mammals have been fed to captive Red Kites in England and, in northern Scotland, fish heads and offal from a local Salmon processing factory have been utilised as a food source.

When the chicks are only 4-5 weeks old, carcasses are chopped into relatively small pieces to ensure that the food is in a form that can be readily ingested. As the chicks grow they quickly become more adept at tearing food for themselves and larger pieces of meat or even whole carcasses can be provided. The young are provisioned with as much food as they can eat and, as would be expected in a natural situation, the amount required tends to drop once the birds are almost fully-grown. At this stage, food is required only for body maintenance rather than to fuel growth. As in the majority of birds of prey, Red Kites derive all the water they need from their food and so it is not necessary to provide captive birds with a source of drinking water.

Perches are provided within each aviary compartment so that when the young birds reach fledging age, at 7-8 weeks, they are able to fly between perches and build up their wing muscles in preparation for their first flights in the wild. Despite their large size, Red Kites are remarkably manoeuvrable and the young birds quickly learn to turn around in mid-air within the aviaries in order to fly several lengths without stopping to land.

In order to ensure that the birds are healthy before release into the wild, they are assessed by veterinary specialists whilst still in the aviaries. Health checks include analysis of blood samples (which also allow the birds to be sexed from their DNA), faecal samples, as well as a full external examination of the individual birds. Few health problems have been encountered but where minor problems are found it is often possible to treat birds using antibiotics to try to maximise their fitness before release. A very small number of birds have been deemed unfit for release as their chances of long-term survival in the wild were considered very poor. These individuals have either been given to a recognized bird of prey centre or euthanased humanely.

Release to the wild

As with any reintroduction, despite all the careful background research and planning, there is an element of uncertainty as to how birds will fare in the wild, especially in the early years of a programme when the release methods are untested. Those responsible for looking after the birds in captivity often admit to having mixed emotions on the day they are to be released. On the one hand, there is immense relief that the birds will, at last, be allowed to fly free in the wild, hopefully the first stage in their becoming an established and familiar part

Table 5: **Food supplied to Red Kites reared and released in southern England in 1990 and 1991** *(from Evans* et al. *1997)*

	1 Jun-28 Jul 1990	7 Jun-10 Aug 1991	25 Jun-27 Jul 1991
No. of days	58	65	32
No. of young Kites	11	11-15	2
Mallard	–	1	–
Common Pheasant	–	3	–
Woodpigeon	15	22	–
Jay	–	4	0
Magpie	81	41	8
Carrion Crow	56	24	1
Rook	20	–	–
Jackdaw	3	1	1
Stoat	4	4	–
Weasel	4	8	–
Fox	10	3	–
Rabbit	129	125	17
Grey Squirrel	18	136	9

of the local landscape. But there is also an understandable element of concern. How will released birds cope with their first days away from the safety of the release pens? Will they find sufficient food and suitable roosting sites? And will they manage to avoid threats such as illegal persecution and electrocution on powerlines, known to result in deaths in other parts of their range?

The young birds are released in groups when about 10-12 weeks old by removing a panel from the front of each aviary compartment. In Scotland, this is usually done before dawn, with the birds able to leave in their own time from first light onwards. In England, the pens are opened during the day, sometimes in the presence of local landowners, farmers and gamekeepers, and others involved in the reintroduction programme. Individual birds exhibit considerable differences in behaviour when faced with the open countryside for the first time. Some fly strongly and within a few minutes are circling over the surrounding area as if inspecting their new surroundings. Others are more circumspect, making only a short and hesitant first flight before coming to rest in a nearby tree.

In most birds of prey, young remain dependent on their parents for several weeks after leaving the nest. The technique of hacking, whereby food is provided at, or close to, the release site until the birds have adapted to finding their own food in the wild, simulates this period of dependence. There tends to be considerable variation in the amount of time that released Red Kites remain dependent on food provided at the aviaries. Some continue to take food for three weeks or more, although they are no doubt also finding alternative sources of food by this stage. Others disperse away from the release area within a few days, and are clearly already fully independent by this stage. The fact that the majority of released Red Kites do not return to the aviaries to take advantage of handouts for more than a few weeks is, initially, rather surprising. It would seem to make more sense for the young birds to take advantage of a guaranteed source of food for as long as it remains available. The most likely explanation is that animal carcasses tend to be unpredictable in their occurrence in the wild and it is therefore unwise for a scavenging bird to rely too heavily on just a single source of food, however reliable it seems to be in the short term. A far safer strategy is to gain a thorough knowledge of the wider area and a range of different places where food sources are present. Then, if one source of food unexpectedly dries up, the birds will already be familiar with alternative sites where food can be obtained. The released Red Kites seem to follow this strategy and once they are familiar with the local area they have no need to return regularly to the aviaries in order to find food.

Some reintroduction projects involve species that rely on specialised hunting techniques and, because released young are deprived of the opportunity to learn such techniques from their parents, survival rates may be reduced. Although projects involving such species, including Peregrine and Osprey, can be successful (see Table 7), the survival rates for released birds are rarely as high as has been the case during the Red Kite programme. The Red Kite's preference for animal carrion, food that can be exploited using relatively simple foraging behaviours, means that a lack of contact with the parent birds is not a serious disadvantage.

Monitoring of released birds

All well-planned reintroductions include a programme of monitoring so that the success, or otherwise, of releases can be assessed. In order to improve the chances of keeping track of released Red Kites, birds have been fitted with plastic, coloured wing-tags marked with a number, letter or symbol (Evans et al. 1997), and radio-transmitters while still in the aviary. The attachments for the wing-tags sometimes weaken with age and tags are often lost after a few years. They nevertheless provide valuable information on dispersal behaviour and survival during the vital first few years after release, by allowing individual birds to be identified up to about 800m away using a telescope.

The radio-transmitters widely used in the early years of the reintroduction programme were attached to the two central tail feathers and were lost when these feathers were moulted out about one year later. More recently, harness-mounted transmitters, with a battery life of about three years, have been used (e.g. Dixon 2001). Radio-transmitters enable very detailed information to be collected on dispersal distances and direction, home range, habitat use and survival rates. Radio-tracking is also useful when studying other aspects of the Red Kite's ecology, allowing, for example, the exact location of roosting and breeding sites to be pinpointed. Some transmitters include a mercury tilt-switch that causes the pulse rate of the radio-signal to change depending on whether the bird is flying (with the tail horizontal) or perched (with the tail vertical). A sustained lack of variation in the signal suggests that the bird has died and radio-tracking can then be used to locate the carcass. This allows post-mortems to be carried out on fresh carcasses and has helped considerably in determining the main causes of mortality for released birds.

The range of the radio-transmitters used on Red Kites varies depending on the nature of the landscape and the activity of the bird. When there is a direct line of sight between the bird and the person with the radio receiver, the range can be as much as 40km or more. This has been exploited by using aerial surveys to search for missing birds as a wide transect on either side of the aircraft can be scanned (Walls & Kenward 1995). On the ground, the range is often over 10km when a Red Kite is flying but this is substantially reduced if the bird perches low down or is on the ground and there is no direct line of sight between the receiver and the transmitter.

Tail-mounted radio-transmitter used to monitor released Red Kites in their first year (Ian Carter)

Figure 4: **Comparison of population increase between southern England and northern Scotland**

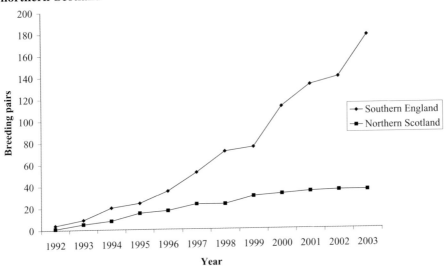

Progress so far

Although the release projects in southern England and northern Scotland were carefully planned and based on methods that had been successful in reintroducing other birds of prey in Europe and the United States, no-one could be certain how well the first groups of released Red Kites would fare. There was therefore considerable relief when monitoring showed that the birds coped well in the wild and a relatively high proportion survived their first year.

From 1989 to 1994, a total of 93 young were released at each of the two initial sites (Chiltern Hills and Black Isle). A minimum of 76% of birds in southern England and 51% of birds in northern Scotland survived their first year (Evans *et al.* 1999) with survival rates for older birds and for birds that remained in the release area during their first year substantially higher. The main loss of reintroduced birds resulted from dispersal away from the release areas, mainly during the first autumn, soon after release, or during the following spring. Some of the dispersing birds subsequently returned, but many did not and are assumed to have perished.

Exceeding the expectations of almost everyone involved in the project, the first breeding attempt in the wild was in southern England in 1991 and the first successful breeding in both release areas was in 1992. In this year, four pairs reared nine young in southern England and one pair reared a single chick in northern Scotland. From then on, population growth in southern England was rapid and, by 2006, the population here had increased to over 300 pairs. Initially, the northern Scotland population also increased steadily, but due to far higher levels of persecution (see Chapter 11), it has not reached anywhere near the levels seen in southern England (Figure 4). The Black Isle population in 2006 was estimated at just 40 pairs, an increase of only seven pairs since 2000. Monitoring has continued in both areas and each year a proportion of nestlings are fitted with wing-tags and a smaller number with radio-transmitters.

Although the reintroduced populations have increased relatively rapidly, they have been slow to spread out and recolonise new areas well away from the release sites. This is partly the result of an inbuilt tendency, found in many birds of prey, for individuals to breed close to where they were reared (or released), and partly because the countryside is so well suited to Red Kites that they are able to thrive at high densities and have little incentive to search out new areas. In order to encourage the spread of Red Kites throughout England and Scotland, birds have now been released at six additional sites and there is a proposal for a further release project in northeast Scotland which could start in 2007. In northern Scotland, small-scale releases have been used in recent years in order to try and encourage spread away from the Black Isle where persecution is currently preventing natural spread. This so-called 'micro-release' project has involved releasing small numbers of young birds within 20km of the core population. It is too early to say whether this new approach will be successful in expanding the breeding range in northern Scotland or whether the birds will simply return to the core population nearby. Full details of all these projects including timescales, numbers released, sources of birds and current population estimates are given in Table 6.

Rehabilitation

Released or wild-fledged Red Kites are sometimes found injured and taken into captivity for veterinary treatment. In some cases, birds have only been recovered because they could be located by radio-tracking and they would otherwise undoubtedly have perished from their injuries. When a population is still small, each individual bird is extremely valuable and successful rehabilitation can make an important contribution to a reintroduction project. This was certainly the case for an adult bird found with shotgun injuries in southern England and released back into the wild in central England in 1995, following rehabilitation at the Institute of Zoology, London Zoo. This individual was a member of the first pair to attempt to breed in central England, in the

Figure 5: **Approximate location of the main release sites in England and Scotland**

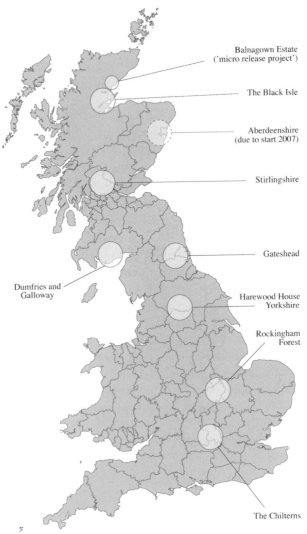

Balnagown Estate
('micro release project')

The Black Isle

Aberdeenshire
(due to start 2007)

Stirlingshire

Gateshead

Dumfries and
Galloway

Harewood House
Yorkshire

Rockingham
Forest

The Chilterns

year following its release, and has since bred successfully on a number of occasions. Another adult bird, again from southern England, was found in very poor condition by a member of the public and, following a period of recuperation in captivity, was released in Yorkshire at the start of a new project in 1999. In 2000, it paired up with a first-year bird and bred successfully, helping to rear the first two young in northern England for well over 100 years.

Reading wing-tags

Wing-tags are fitted to all birds released during the reintroduction programme and continue to be fitted to a proportion of wild-fledged young in the re-established populations and in Wales. They may be read on a perched bird at close range with binoculars and at up to about 800m away, in good light conditions, using a telescope. Only by recording the tag colours, together with the number, letter or symbol marked on the tag can an individual bird be identified. But by simply recording the colour of the tag on each wing it is at least possible to find out from which of the release areas a bird originated and in which year it was released or fledged. The colour of the tag on the left wing indicates the area as follows:

Southern England, Chilterns	Yellow
Central England, Northamptonshire	White
Northern England, Yorkshire	Orange
Northeast England, Gateshead	Pink
Southern Scotland, Dumfries & Galloway	Green
Central Scotland, Stirlingshire	Red
Northern Scotland, Black Isle	Blue
Wales	Black

The colour of the right wing-tag indicates the year in which the bird was fledged or released and is the same across all areas in each year (2000 - Pink; 2001 - Blue; 2002 - White; 2003 - Red; 2004 - Yellow; 2005 - Orange; 2006 - Green; 2007 - Purple). Each wing-tag has a bar across the base which is the same colour as the tag on the opposite wing. This allows a perched individual to be identified even if only one of the bird's wing-tags can be seen.

The wider benefits of reintroducing Red Kites

As a result of its impressive size, relatively confiding behaviour, and attractive plumage, the Red Kite has become extremely popular in the release areas. Some people have even taken to feeding Red Kites and delight in attracting them to scraps of food on the garden lawn – an echo of days gone by when they were common scavengers around human settlements. The popularity of the bird has led to a high demand for information about this new addition to the landscape.

Table 6: **Summary of the Red Kite Reintroduction Programme in Britain**

Release area	Timescale and number of birds released	Origin of birds	First successful breeding	Breeding pairs in 2006	Comments
The Chilterns (Oxfordshire, Buckinghamshire), southern England	1989-94: 93	82 from Aragón and Navarra, northern Spain; 7 from Wales; 4 from Skåne, southern Sweden	1992	>300	One of the two initial release sites. By far the largest reintroduced population; the Red Kite is now a common and familiar bird across large areas of the Chilterns
The Black Isle, northern Scotland	1989-93: 93	Skåne, southern Sweden	1992	40	Beset by problems due to illegal persecution. Population only a fraction of that in the Chilterns despite the same number of birds being released
Rockingham Forest, Northamptonshire, central England	1995-98: 70	35 from Segovia, Salamanca and Valladolid, central Spain; 33 from the Chilterns; 2 from Wales	1997	74	The first project to utilise young birds from the re-established Chilterns population. Now the second largest reintroduced population
Stirlingshire, central Scotland	1996-01: 103	Sachsen-Anhalt and Sachsen, Germany	1998	28	Self-sustaining population now established but rate of increase slowed by illegal persecution
Harewood House, near Leeds, Yorkshire, northern England	1999-03: 69	The Chilterns	2000	40	The smallest number of birds released by any of the main projects but rapid increase in breeding numbers

Table 6: **Summary of the Red Kite Reintroduction Programme in Britain** *(continued)*

Release area	Timescale and number of birds released	Origin of birds	First success-ful breeding	Breeding pairs in 2006	Comments
Dumfries & Galloway, southern Scotland	2001-05: 104	56 from the Black Isle; 41 from the Chilterns; 7 from Sachsen, Germany	2003	17	Slow to take off but breeding population now well established
'Northern Kites', near Gateshead, northeast England	2004-06: 94	The Chilterns	2006	5	The first release site close to a major urban centre with the aim of developing public interest in Red Kites and other raptors. Red Kites have become a common sight on the fringes of Newcastle-upon-Tyne
Aberdeenshire, northeast Scotland	Starting 2007?	The Black Isle, central Scotland and the Chilterns?	n/a	n/a	Likely to be close to the major urban centre of Aberdeen
Balnagown Estate, Easter Ross, northeast Scotland	2005-ongoing: 24 birds released 2005-06	The Black Isle	n/a	n/a	A new approach involving the release of small numbers of birds (all radio-tagged) close to an existing population to aid recolonisation – so-called 'micro-release' project

Project partners and supporters include: British Airways, Conoco, Dumfries & Galloway Raptor Study Group, Forestry Commission, Gateshead Council, Gobierno de Aragón, Gobierno de Navarra, Harewood Estate, Junta de Castilla y León, Martin Luther University, National Trust, Natural England, Northumbrian Water, Royal Air Force, RSPB, Sachsen-Anhalt Lande, Scottish Natural Heritage, Skånes Ornitologiska Förening, Southern England Kite Group, Swedish National Environment Protection Board, Welsh Kite Trust, WWF Sweden and Yorkshire Water.

Local initiatives have been set up in several areas in England and Scotland to provide this information and to help raise awareness of local wildlife and landscapes, using the Red Kite as the central theme. These include Red Kite trails, guided walks, feeding stations and visitor centres with live pictures from a nearby Red Kite nest. The Galloway Kite Trail in southern Scotland was established in 2003 and, according to a study carried out by Glasgow University, by 2006, visitors to the trail were generating up to £750,000 in extra income each year for local businesses. The Red Kite has clearly joined the Osprey, Golden Eagle and White-tailed Sea Eagle as a major attraction for visitors to the Scottish countryside. In 2006, one of the first breeding pairs established by the 'Northern Kites' project nested close to a public footpath on the edge of Gateshead, Newcastle-upon-Tyne. A viewing point was set up during the breeding season and almost 11,000 people visited the site to admire, at close range, this new addition to the local landscape.

One of the benefits of the Red Kite's huge appeal is that its popularity can be harnessed to encourage a greater understanding of the needs of wildlife more generally and the importance of protecting what remains of our local wildlife habitats. This 'flagship species' approach (to use modern conservation jargon), has undoubtedly helped to increase the value that people place on their local countryside and the wildlife it supports, as well as helping to highlight the threats that birds of prey and other predators and scavengers unfortunately still face (Carter 2005). Red Kites have proved to be especially vulnerable to illegal persecution, notably the use of poison baits, and accidental poisoning by highly toxic modern rat poisons (see Chapter 11). Its popularity has given added impetus to initiatives trying to tackle these problems, benefiting not only the Red Kite itself but also a range of other wildlife affected by the same problems.

Reintroducing Red Kites elsewhere

Proposals are well-advanced to build on the success of the reintroduction programme in Britain by trying to re-establish the Red Kite in Ireland. There is good evidence that the Red Kite was present in Ireland in the past, mainly through the existence of Irish names for the bird (D'Arcy 1999), although it was wiped out by human persecution before reliable records were kept. There is little doubt that there is sufficient nesting habitat and an adequate food supply to support a thriving population. Assuming that the necessary licences can be obtained it is hoped that projects will begin simultaneously in Northern Ireland and the Republic of Ireland, possibly starting in 2007, and most likely using young birds taken from nests in Wales.

Further afield, a project to reintroduce the Red Kite to the 'Tocchi' State Natural Reserve in Tuscany, central Italy, began in 1995, led by the National Forest Service (Allavena *et al.* 1996). Red Kites were once common in the area but were wiped out by persecution, mainly shooting and poisoning, during the 1960s. The habitat remained suitable and, as a result of a considerable reduction in the use of poisoned baits, it was thought that the area could, once again, support a viable population. Unlike the programme in England and Scotland, releases involved rehabilitated Red Kites, donated by the authorities in Spain, rather than nestlings taken from the wild. The first five birds were released in June 1996 following a period of nine months spent in aviaries at the release site. Although some birds had to be recaptured because they were unable to fly properly, others were ranging up to 4-5km away from the aviaries one month after release. Food was provided close to the release site and the birds continued to return to the aviaries in late afternoon to roost. Unfortunately, it is not thought that any of the birds survived for long enough to begin breeding in the wild.

A new project, based on a captive population of 12 Red Kites, began in the Regional Natural Park Gola della Rossa and Frasassi in central Italy in 2000. Two pairs of birds bred successfully in captivity and eight of the resulting young were released into the wild, four in March and four in July. Radio-tracking showed that the birds remained in the vicinity of the release site for at least the first few months after release (Angelini *et al*. 2001). Red Kites still breed in parts of central Italy and there are some conservationists in Italy who believe that efforts should be focussed on protecting this population effectively, rather than trying to reintroduce birds nearby.

Raptor reintroductions in Europe

Table 7 shows the wide variety of reintroduction projects, involving at least ten different birds of prey (in addition to the Red Kite), that have taken place, or are currently in progress, in Europe. The majority of projects have been based upon the hacking of young birds, either bred in captivity or collected from the wild. With many species, the use of young birds collected from suitable donor populations in the wild is the most straightforward option as captive breeding requires considerable expertise, is time consuming and also relatively expensive. The use of wild-taken young also carries a reduced risk that the birds will become imprinted on humans. The young spend the critical first few weeks of life being reared naturally in the wild and spend only a short period of time in captivity before they are released. Most projects involving birds of prey that still have healthy wild populations remaining in parts of Europe have used this approach.

Projects involving the three species of vulture have utilised captive-bred birds, mainly because these species became so rare in the wild that collecting sufficient young for a reintroduction programme was not a sustainable option. This was particularly true with the Bearded Vulture (or Lammergeier) project in the Alps. By setting up a captive breeding programme involving a number of facilities across Europe it has been possible to release more than 130 birds into the wild. This compares with a total European breeding population estimated at only 86 pairs in the mid-1990s (Hagemeijer & Blair 1997). Projects involving the Peregrine have also made use of captive-bred birds as the long history of captive breeding by falconers has ensured a ready supply of young for release.

Young birds must make the transition from dependence on their parents to surviving on their own and at this age they are pre-programmed to learn how to find food and to fend for themselves. Reintroduction projects benefit from releasing birds that are close to their natural fledging age, as full advantage is taken of this stage in their development and, as a result, survival rates are often high. Older birds are likely to do less well, particularly captive-reared birds, which may find it more difficult to adapt to life in the wild, not only because of their age but also the prolonged period of time they have spent in captivity. However, there is one advantage in releasing adult birds in that, if they do survive, breeding in the wild is likely to begin sooner than is the case when young birds are released. This can make a significant difference in larger species such as vultures, where birds make their first breeding attempt only when they reach five or six years of age. The Griffon Vulture project in southern France involved the release of some captive-reared adult birds and resulted in successful breeding in the wild only a few months after the first birds were released (Terrasse *et al.* 2004).

Cross-fostering, where the young or eggs from one species are placed in the nest of another, has been used with Peregrines and Lesser Kestrels. In the case of the Peregrine in Germany, some of the young birds were placed in wild Goshawk nests in an attempt to re-establish a tree-nesting population of Peregrines. Despite concerns that a bird's behaviour could be altered if it is reared by adults of a separate species, there has been some initial success using this technique although tree-nesting Peregrines have yet to become re-established.

Some people have reservations about using reintroductions in order to restore lost species, seeing such projects as unnatural human interference, or believing that valuable conservation resources would be better spent on other things. One bird magazine in Britain has gone as far as using the prefix 'real' when referring to Red Kites in Wales as if to suggest that the reintroduced birds are less worthy of attention. Whilst it is easy to understand that seeing a Red Kite that has recently been freed from an aviary is less satisfying for some people than watching a wild-fledged bird, untainted by human hands, in mid-Wales, it is important to try and take a longer-term view of what may be achieved by reintroduction. Almost 20 years on from the start of the reintroduction programme, Red Kites are now breeding freely again in seven different areas of England and Scotland. These populations will hopefully continue to increase and spread out to new areas without further assistance and the role played by humans in their initial establishment will increasingly be forgotten. A countryside without Red Kites is actually the more unnatural situation, as it is the direct result of past human interference and persecution on a huge scale. Without the reintroduction projects this unnatural situation would have persisted for many decades more and a large number of people would have been deprived of the opportunity to watch such a spectacular species in their local countryside.

Table 7: Bird of prey reintroduction projects in Europe
(see Cade (2000) for a full review of reintroduction projects involving diurnal birds of prey worldwide)

Species	Area	Dates	Reintroduction methods	Progress	Organisations involved	Comments/further information
White-tailed Sea Eagle	Island of Rum and mainland of western Scotland	1975-1998	Nestlings taken from Norway and hacked from release pens	82 birds released 1975-1985; a further 58 birds released 1993-1998. First successful breeding 1985. 33 pairs reared 29 young in 2006	Scottish Natural Heritage and RSPB	Earlier small-scale releases on Fair Isle unsuccessful. Coordinated programme began in 1975. New projects planned for eastern Scotland, eastern England and Republic of Ireland could start in 2007/2008. Bainbridge *et al.* (2003)
Golden Eagle	Glenveagh National Park, Donegal, Republic of Ireland	2001-ongoing	Nestlings taken from Scotland and hacked from release site	46 birds released 2001-2006. Two pairs laid eggs in 2006 but no successful breeding so far	Irish Raptor Study Groups and The Curlew Trust	Some initial concern that birds would predate livestock dealt with through liaison with landowners. Several birds fitted with satellite tags. O'Toole *et al.* (2002)
Goshawk	Britain	From 1960s	Birds used for falconry, many imported from northern and central Europe, escaped or released	Estimated 250+ birds released/escaped. c. 350-400 pairs by late 1990s	Mostly individual falconers	Lack of organised release programme with monitoring so relative importance of releases and natural recolonisation not known. Kenward (2006)
Common Buzzard	Norfolk and Sussex, England	From 1994	Hacking nestlings taken from wild at artificial nests at release sites	Over 40 birds released by 1997; dispersal patterns and survival rates similar to wild populations; several breeding pairs established involving at least one released bird	Centre for Ecology and Hydrology	An experimental project to facilitate study of dispersal and survival in low density populations

Table 7: **Bird of prey reintroduction projects in Europe** *(continued)*
(see Cade (2000) for a full review of reintroduction projects involving diurnal birds of prey worldwide)

Species	Area	Dates	Reintroduction methods	Progress	Organisations involved	Comments/further information
Osprey	Rutland Water, central England	1996-2005	Nestlings taken from Scotland and hacked from pens at release site	64 birds released 1996-2001. A further 11 birds released 2005, mostly females, in attempt to restore imbalance in sexes. First successful breeding in 2001. One pair reared 3 young in 2006	Leicestershire and Rutland Wildlife Trust, Anglian Water and Highland Foundation for Wildlife	Two birds released at Rutland Water bred successfully with wild birds in Wales in 2004. Programme of satellite tracking to follow progress of birds on migration. Dennis (1996) and subsequent project reports
Osprey	Cadiz, Andalusia, southern Spain	2003-ongoing	Nestlings taken from Scotland, Germany and Finland, hacked at reservoir release site	At least 25 birds released so far	Andalusian government and international partners	Pair bred successfully at release site in 2005, thought to be wild birds attracted to the site by presence of released juveniles. New project planned in Tuscany, Italy, involving young taken from Corsica. Additional projects proposed for Germany, Spain and Sardinia
Griffon Vulture	Abruzzi Region, Central Apennines, Italy	From 1994	Involved release of rehabilitated adult and immature birds from Spain	57 birds released by 1997; high survival rates and low levels of dispersal. First successful breeding in 1997. Birds also released at new site c.50km from the first, starting 2001	Corpo Forestale dello Stato (National Forest Service)	Unusual project in that releases involved mainly adult and sub-adult birds

Table 7: **Bird of prey reintroduction projects in Europe** *(continued)*
(see Cade (2000) for a full review of reintroduction projects involving diurnal birds of prey worldwide)

Species	Area	Dates	Reintroduction methods	Progress	Organisations involved	Comments/further information
Griffon Vulture	Massif Central, southern France	1980-1998	Captive-reared adult and immature birds hacked from cages at several release sites	111 birds released. First breeding in 1980-82. 110 breeding pairs, 87 fledglings in 2003	Fond's d'Intervention pour les Rapaces	Following unsuccessful trials involving juveniles in 1970, releases involved high proportion of adult birds. Food provided for birds in long term, not just immediately following release. Terrasse *et al.* (2004)
Griffon Vulture	Southern 'pre' Alps, south-east France	From 1996	Captive-reared adult and immature birds hacked from cages at three release sites	86 birds released by 2002. First successful breeding in 1999. 42 breeding pairs, 23 young fledged in 2003	Fond's d'Intervention pour les Rapaces	Based on same methods as Massif Central project (see above). Terrasse *et al.* (2004)
Black Vulture	Massif Central, southern France	1992-2002	Involved captive-bred young and older birds as well as some wild-taken young from Spain. Birds hacked from cages	47 birds released. First successful breeding by released birds aged four years in 1996. 19 young produced in the wild in 2003	Black Vulture Conservation Foundation (BVCF) and Fond's d'Intervention pour les Rapaces	Same release area as for Griffon Vulture project - see above BVCF also operates a restocking programme in Majorca to help conserve its threatened Black Vulture population. Terrasse *et al.* (2004)
Bearded Vulture	Austrian, French, Italian and Swiss Alps	1986-ongoing	Captive-bred young birds hacked from release sites	137 birds released by 2005; high survival rates and low dispersal. First successful breeding in 1997. Wild population of c.110 birds by 2005	IUCN, WWF and a number of different captive-breeding centres	Captive-breeding adopted to obtain birds for release as population in wild reduced to very low level. New project in Sierra de Cazorla, southern Spain, started in 2006

Table 7: **Bird of prey reintroduction projects in Europe** *(continued)*
(see Cade (2000) for a full review of reintroduction projects involving diurnal birds of prey worldwide)

Species	Area	Dates	Reintroduction methods	Progress	Organisations involved	Comments/further information
Peregrine	Germany (similar work in northwest Poland)	From 1977	Captive-bred young hacked from release sites, including buildings. Artificial tree nests used to encourage restoration of tree-nesting population. Some birds cross-fostered into wild Goshawk nests	Over 800 birds released. About 700 pairs re-established by 2003	Private initiative by Deutscher Falkenorden with support from government agencies	Release of large numbers of birds possible due to large captive population and well-established captive-breeding techniques. Breeding on cliffs and buildings. Tree-nesting population has not yet become re-established
Peregrine	Sweden and southeast Norway	From 1982	Captive-bred young hacked from release sites or fostered into wild Peregrine nests	Over 400 birds released. About 115 pairs by 2003, population increasing	Swedish Society of Nature Conservation, Swedish Environment Protection Board and others	Release of large numbers of birds possible due to large captive population and well-established captive-breeding techniques
Lesser Kestrel	Catalonia, Spain	From 1989	Mainly captive-bred young either hacked or cross-fostered into Common Kestrel nests	More than 700 birds released. Over 70% survived first year. First breeding in 1990. c.30 pairs by 1998	Sevei de Protecció i Gestió de la Fauna, Direcció General del Medi Natural	Some initial problems with secondary poisoning

The publicity surrounding the Red Kite reintroduction programme has encouraged others to consider undertaking local releases of Red Kites. Several bird of prey centres now hold pairs of adult Red Kites, often made up of birds found injured that are not fit for return to the wild. Although it has proved very difficult to breed from these birds, there has been some limited success in recent years and at least one centre, near Andover in Hampshire, has already released a small number of captive-bred young and rehabilitated adults into the surrounding countryside. There are certainly dangers associated with this approach, not least because of the difficulties in rearing young in captivity without the birds becoming imprinted on humans or overly familiar with human structures. This has been a huge problem for those involved in the California Condor project, with captive-bred birds found to be at high risk of electrocution through an apparent association with man-made structures and a resulting tendency to perch on electricity poles. Some released California Condors have also been found wandering around campsites in search of food having clearly lost much of the natural fear of humans that exists in wild-bred birds (Snyder & Snyder 2000). Wild Red Kites are not especially wary of humans compared with the majority of birds of prey and they often forage around villages and the edges of towns. The potential for tame or imprinted captive-bred birds to take this one stage further and actively

solicit food from people is a serious concern and something that needs to be avoided at all costs if the Red Kite is to retain its popularity.

Perhaps surprisingly, there are currently no legal restrictions on releasing captive-bred Red Kites in Britain and this may need to be addressed in future by amending the existing legislation. Adding the Red Kite to Schedule 9 of the Wildlife and Countryside Act (1981) would be a relatively simple first step and would mean that releases would be illegal unless covered by an appropriate licence. This was done for Barn Owl in 1992 to prevent further inappropriate releases of this species and the associated high mortality of released birds (Cayford & Percival 1992, Carter & Newbery 2004). Adding Red Kite to Schedule 9 would not necessarily preclude the release of captive-bred birds but would provide a mechanism for ensuring that projects only went ahead if they were undertaken with adequate planning and if the problems associated with captive-breeding had been adequately addressed.

adult

juvenile

adult

Black
Kite

juvenile

juvenile

adult

DAN POWELL

*Adult and juvenile Red Kites are readily separable in the field if they are seen at close range
(see Chapter 1 for key differences)*

1. *Adult Red Kite. Note the rich, reddish-brown plumage on the body and wing-coverts, with heavy black streaks on the underbody*   *(Chris Gomersall)*

2. *Juvenile Red Kite. The 'washed-out' appearance and pale-fringed wing-coverts forming an obvious line on the upperwing show that this is a first-year bird*   *(Chris Gomersall)*

3. *Black Kite. The less deeply forked tail, darker plumage and six, rather than five, obvious 'fingers' at the wing-tips clearly distinguish the Black Kite from its closest relative*

(Dick Forsman)

4. *Juvenile Red Kite. Resting birds are often harder to age than birds in flight but note the dull eye, 'washed-out' plumage and pale line formed by the tips of the wing-coverts (Mike Lane)*

5. *Twelve-week-old Red Kites inside their aviary just before being released into the wild*
(Ian Carter)

6. *A young Red Kite making its first flight from the release aviary in Northamptonshire, central England* *(Ian Carter)*

Chapter 6

DIET AND FEEDING BEHAVIOUR

The Red Kite is a supreme generalist and opportunist scavenger, taking advantage of whatever food sources are locally available and accessible. As a result, it has been able to exploit a very wide range of habitats, from the grimy streets of medieval London to the rain-soaked hills of central Wales and the hot, dry, Iberian plains – in each area depending on a very different diet.

Some live prey is taken, particularly during the breeding season, but the Red Kite is not a powerful or aggressive bird, and is certainly no threat to livestock or full-grown gamebirds. As an opportunist scavenger, however, it is often the first bird on the scene when an animal dies and it is easy to see how, with its large wing-span, hooked beak and sharp claws, it acquired an unfair reputation with farmers and gamekeepers in the past.

Food spectrum and requirements

With the possible exception of its closest relative the Black Kite, the Red Kite is unrivalled by any other European bird of prey in its ability to exploit such a wide variety of different prey. Here is a bird that can be seen snatching crane-flies from the air and delicately transferring them from foot to bill in a manner more befitting a Hobby, but can also be found in the company of vultures in southern Spain, feasting on the carcasses of dead cattle. Detailed studies of diet in various parts of its range have shown that the Red Kite will feed on almost any type of animal carrion that it comes across and a full list of species recorded would extend to many pages. Birds and mammals form the bulk of the diet in most areas but invertebrates, fish, reptiles and amphibians are all taken when available. Lord Lilford (1883) was quick to recognise the Red Kite's scavenging tendencies and also knew that it was, in no sense, a fussy eater:

Literally nothing that any bird will eat comes amiss to the Kite; and from my acquaintance with him in captivity, I am inclined to think that he prefers his food somewhat high. I have seen a Kite devour rotten cabbage-stalks, scraps of bread, potatoes, fish, flesh, and fowl, fresh, high and putrid, and complacently swallow pieces of stiff leather.

Live prey is limited to invertebrates and other creatures small or weak enough to be overpowered by a bird not noted for its strength. Small mammals, up to the size of half-grown Rabbits are sometimes taken, as are small and medium-sized birds, particularly nestlings or recently fledged and inexperienced young.

The amount of food required each day varies, depending on factors such as temperature, stage of moult and the amount of energy expended during routine daily activities. As a rough estimate, larger birds of prey including kites, buzzards and eagles require around 10% or less of their body weight in food each day (Barton & Houston 1993), suggesting a figure of around 80-120g for a full-grown Red Kite. This is rather less than the estimate of 130-140g given by Brown (1970) but consistent with the estimate of Bustamante (1994) of 'less than 100g' as a daily requirement. Birds in captivity, where food intake is easy to measure, appear to consume rather more than this. A Red Kite trained to fly at the National Bird of Prey Centre in Newent, Gloucestershire, consumed 4-6 one-day-old chicks each day, totaling 100-180g (Walters Davis & Davis

1973), and two captive birds studied by Barton and Houston (1993) consumed an average of 160g and 180g daily when fed on day-old chicks.

Barton and Houston (1993) measured the digestive efficiency of a wide range of predatory birds in captivity and found that the Red Kite had the longest intestine and one of the most efficient digestive systems of all the birds of prey studied. They attributed this to the Red Kite's generalist diet and its tendency to rely on carrion which is a poorer quality food than freshly killed prey. The availability of carrion is also often unpredictable and so it is important that, when found, its value is maximised through efficient digestion. In contrast, birds that actively hunt live prey have a shorter and less efficient digestive system. This reduces weight and so is more compatible with the need for fast hunting flights. The reduced digestive efficiency in birds of prey with active hunting methods is compensated for by the higher quality of food derived from live prey and the fact that its availability is more predictable than that of carrion.

Observations of feeding Red Kites using cameras set up at nest sites, show that with small and medium-sized prey, the whole carcass is often consumed rather than being torn into pieces. For example, well grown chicks on a nest in central England swallowed small and medium-sized mammals whole, including a Weasel and even half a Brown Rat, the latter taking several minutes to tackle with only the tail visible hanging out of the beak. Large pieces of skin, fur and bone of animals such as Rabbit were also swallowed whole. Similar observations have been made with birds in captivity. When Brown Rats were fed to captive birds there was a preference for certain parts of the carcass, including the liver and small intestines, but all parts were eventually consumed including the large intestines, tail and head (Craig Brakes pers. comm.). This behaviour is sensible for a bird with a powerful digestive system, allowing full benefit to be obtained from the food available. It is also likely that valuable nutrients and minerals are derived from ingesting carcasses which include skin and bone. Those parts of an animal that the Red Kite is unable to fully digest, including fur, feathers and pieces of bone, are regurgitated as pellets which are commonly found at nest and roost sites.

Foraging techniques

In order to exploit a wide variety of both animal carrion and live prey, a range of different foraging methods are employed. Active hunting is only infrequently witnessed but other types of behaviour are readily observed, and help to make the Red Kite such an obvious and familiar species. Flight associated with foraging differs from the type of flight seen when a bird is travelling directly from one place to another. In such direct flights the bird usually proceeds purposefully in a straight line and, particularly if there is an adverse wind, uses deep, fluid wing-beats, with a noticeable rising and falling body movement, reminiscent of the flight of a tern. When travelling from place to place in more favourable conditions, circling may be used as an initial means of gaining height before heading off in a straight line glide towards the destination.

Red Kites can be seen searching for food throughout daylight hours. Studies that involved the systematic recording of activity levels throughout the day have suggested that there may be a slight peak in activity in the morning. The average number of birds recorded visiting an experimental feeding station in southern England during the breeding season peaked during the period between 09.00 and 13.00, although birds were present from 06.00 until 20.00 with a gradual decline in activity during the afternoon and evening (Ntampakis & Carter 2005). A similar pattern was found in winter in central England with a peak in foraging activity from the time of initial departure from the roost, when fully light, until around midday (Ottway 2002).

Circling, gliding and hovering

The Red Kite's light frame and long wings and tail enable it to soar effortlessly for long periods by utilising the wind or rising thermals of air. Given suitable conditions, a Red Kite can circle up to several hundred metres with barely a single flap of its wings and thus very little expenditure of energy. High circling is therefore a very efficient method of searching for animal carcasses and allows a large area to be scanned in a relatively short space of time. Blanco (1982) found that Red Kites in southern Spain spent approximately 65% of their flying time higher than 20m above the ground and were often seen circling at far greater heights than this.

A few birds of prey, including the American Turkey Vulture for example, have a keen sense of smell which is used to detect animal carrion at great distance. The Red Kite, as with all other European birds of prey, does not have this ability and must rely instead on its extremely sharp eyesight to locate food. As well as looking for carrion itself, birds also look for signs that other carrion-feeding birds, including other Red Kites, have located a food source. A group of birds circling low over the same area may indicate that a carcass has been found and will be visible at a much greater distance than the dead animal itself (see Chapter 9). Once food has been located, it is approached gradually by descending in ever-tighter circles until only a few metres above the ground. There is often a great reluctance to land because, in contrast to its aerial agility, the Red Kite, with its long tail and relatively small feet, is rather ungainly and awkward on the ground and is potentially vulnerable to ground predators. Where possible, the carcass may be snatched up from the ground and carried to a safe feeding perch or, with very small carcasses, even devoured on the wing. The Red Kite is extremely agile in flight and can drop down rapidly with wings folded back, to snatch up food items from confined spaces, for example close to hedges or buildings, where it would be very wary of landing on the ground. With larger carcasses, too heavy to lift, Red Kites will often land a few metres away and approach cautiously on foot before beginning to feed.

When searching for smaller carcasses or invertebrates, birds fly much closer to the ground and can frequently be seen gliding just a few metres above the fields, head tilted downwards, scanning the ground below. Earthworms are a favourite food and in damp conditions, often early in the morning, several birds may gather over a suitable field, sometimes in the company of Buzzards, to take earthworms that have emerged from their burrows. Red Kites can be watched dropping down from 10m or more above the ground to take an earthworm only a few centimetres long, showing just how good their eyesight must be. Brief hovering flights are used occasionally to inspect a potential food item more closely before landing, and Red Kites will, at times, hang almost motionless into the wind, in order to scan the ground below in more detail.

Walking

Buzzards frequently walk or hop along the ground when searching for invertebrates and this technique is sometimes adopted by the Red Kite, perhaps mainly as a means of conserving energy when low temperatures and lack of wind make flying for prolonged periods more arduous. As when scavenging on animal carcasses, Red Kites feeding on invertebrates often land a few metres away from food they have located from the air and then walk up to it.

Active hunting

Low gliding and flapping flight is occasionally used in the pursuit of live prey, although observations of anything other than invertebrates being killed are uncommon. Davis and Davis (1981) reported several examples where birds up to the size of a Rook were chased and killed, with prey being taken either on the ground or in the air. The Red Kite is capable of rapid aerial pursuits, at least over a short distance, but most prey is taken by surprise rather than following a chase of any length. Prey is apparently mainly dispatched using the bill rather than the claws (Glutz von Blotzheim *et al.* 1971).

The Red Kite's relative lack of strength and aggression restricts the size of animals that are taken and, as Yarrell (1857) describes, may prevent the predation of even small prey:

The Kite, like the Sparrow-Hawk, frequently visits the poultry-yard, but is not remarkable for its courage: Hens have been known by their vociferations and their show of resistance to protect their chicks from the threatened attack, and even to drive away the unwelcome intruder.

Only rarely will a Red Kite resort to 'perch and wait' tactics, so favoured by birds like the Kestrel and Buzzard. These species are less well adapted than the Red Kite for remaining in the air for long periods, and watching from a perch for passing prey is an effective, low-cost hunting technique. The Red Kite's dependence on carrion means that active foraging is required to locate food and the bird's lightweight frame and supreme aerial ability makes it well suited to this task.

Food piracy

Anyone who has visited one of the feeding stations in mid-Wales or Scotland will be aware that Red Kites come by some of their food by stealing it from other birds (known as kleptoparasitism). When a fellow scavenger, often a Carrion Crow or Magpie, is seen flying with a piece of food, the waiting Red Kite flies from its perch and begins a rapid, skua-like pursuit, making full use of its aerial agility. In trying to escape, the target bird may drop the food and the Red Kite then spirals down to take it, sometimes before it has even reached the ground. By pirating food from other birds, there is less need to land among the unseemly mêlées of scavenging birds that often develop close to a source of food, where a lack of strength and aggression is a serious disadvantage. At a large carcass, where the weak-billed Red Kite may have difficulty in tearing pieces of flesh for itself, this feeding strategy allows it to exploit the more powerful, but less agile, scavengers present in order to gain a share of food that might otherwise be unavailable.

It is not only members of the crow family that are vulnerable to having food stolen in this way. Snow and Perrins (1998) noted Grey Heron, Buzzard, Osprey, Goshawk, Peregrine, Hobby and White-tailed Sea Eagle as victims of the Red Kite and Wildman *et al.* (1998) added Kestrel and Sparrowhawk to the list from their observations in northern Scotland. The Kestrel was robbed of a Brown Rat when on the ground, whilst the Sparrowhawk was robbed in flight of a Blackbird, presumably requiring an element of surprise in order to get the better of such an accomplished flier. Gómez-Tejedor (1998) studied foraging by scavengers at a rubbish dump in Badajoz, Spain, and recorded incidents of Red Kites attempting to steal food from Cattle Egrets, White Storks and Lesser Black-backed Gulls.

In some cases, food may be obtained from other species without the need to steal it directly and as long ago as 1939, Uttendörfer recorded Red Kites scavenging on prey remains at a Peregrine nest. The aggressive way in which most intruders into a Peregrine's territory are dealt with is probably the main reason why this type of behaviour has not been recorded more frequently.

Red Kites sometimes fall victim to food piracy themselves. The White-tailed Sea Eagle is mentioned by Cramp and Simmons (1980) as stealing food from a Red Kite, and at feeding stations, where large numbers of scavenging birds gather, Red Kites often lose food items to crows or, indeed, to other Red Kites. In this situation, food items may change hands several times before they are finally consumed.

Methods of studying diet

Diet is usually determined in birds of prey by a combination of analysis of regurgitated pellets, examining food remains found at roost or nest sites, and direct observation of foraging birds. Each method provides different information and each has its own inherent biases (e.g. Simmons *et al*. 1991).

Pellets are relatively easy to find at communal winter roosts and at nest sites where they are produced by both the adults and well-grown nestlings. They contain indigestible material such as fur, feathers and fragments of bone from which prey can be identified, sometimes requiring the use of a high-powered microscope. Potential biases arise from differences in the amount of material that is ingested when different prey types are consumed and from variation in the durability of remains. Fur, for example, tends to survive better than feathers in the acidic stomach of raptors and so the importance of birds in the diet may be underestimated from studies of pellets. In some species of owl which swallow all their prey whole, remains found in pellets can be used to determine the amount of each prey item consumed, with each skull, for example, representing a single individual that has been ingested (Yalden & Morris 1990). This is not possible when looking at Red Kite pellets as prey is not always swallowed whole. Rabbit fur in a pellet clearly indicates that this species has been eaten but could be derived from a medium-sized animal eaten in its entirety or just a few scraps of meat taken from a carcass already largely consumed by other animals.

Examining the remains of food at roost or nest sites provides useful informa- tion on the size as well as species of prey taken, but is heavily biased towards larger prey where the remains are more obvious and therefore more likely to be found. Small prey such as invertebrates, small mammals and birds may be swallowed whole, leaving no trace of remains to be found as evidence.

Direct observation of foraging birds is the only means of determining not only the types of food taken but also how it is obtained. It can, for example, reveal the extent to which prey is taken as carrion rather than actively hunted, and provides information on the importance of invertebrates such as earthworms, the remains of which do not always show up in pellets and are unlikely to be found at nest sites. However, this method is also likely to underestimate the importance of small prey as these may be picked up and carried to a secluded feeding perch, or quickly swallowed whole, making observation less likely. A bird feeding on the ground at a larger carcass may be present for some time and is therefore more likely to be observed.

Pellets regurgitated at communal roosts and nest sites provide valuable information on diet (Ian Carter)

Breeding season diet

In Table 8 each food-type is ranked as of low, medium or high importance in the diet on the basis of the information available. Whilst this, at times, required a rather subjective judgement, it at least gives an indication of relative importance and allows comparisons to be made between four different areas within the Red Kite's European range. Food-types are grouped into categories in the table, as a full list of prey species would extend to many pages for each of the different areas. Most of the information is derived from studies of food remains and analysis of pellets, methods which do not reveal whether prey has been taken as

Table 8: **Breeding season diet in Wales, central England, Germany (several different areas combined) and Doñana National Park, southern Spain (Importance in diet ranked as *High, Medium* or *Low*)**
Information from Carter & Clarke (unpubl.), Carter & Grice (2002), Davis & Davis (1981), Delibes & Garcia (1984), Hille (1995b), Ortlieb (1989), Veiga & Hiraldo (1990) and Tony Cross (pers. comm.)

Food type	Wales	Central England	Southern Spain	Germany
Large mammals	*High:* Dominated by sheep carrion, including docked tails, scrota and placenta	*Low:* Sheep and deer carcasses occasionally scavenged	*Medium:* Including domestic and wild mammals	*Low:* Including Wild Boar, Badger, Roe Deer and domestic species
Lagomorph (Rabbits and hares)	*High:* Rabbits about 6 times more common in diet than Brown Hares	*High:* Mainly Rabbits, fewer Brown Hares	*High:* Rabbits common in diet, hares also taken frequently, mostly juveniles	*High:* Hares more common in diet than Rabbits
Brown Rat	*Medium*	*High:* Some scavenged from around farm buildings	*Medium*	*Medium*
Other small/medium-sized mammals	*High:* Field Vole and other small mammals frequently recorded; also Mole and Hedgehog	*High:* Field Vole the most numerous small mammal; larger species including Mink, Stoat, Weasel, Mole, Hedgehog and Grey Squirrel	*Medium:* Mostly small mammals	*High:* Hamsters are important in some areas; Common Voles also very important
Waterbirds	*Medium:* Black-headed Gull chicks taken from colony by some pairs	*Low*	*High:* Large numbers of Coot taken along with variety of other species, including nestling herons	*Medium:* Variety of different species recorded
Corvids	*High*	*High:* Many taken as nestlings or recently fledged young	*Medium:* Mainly Magpies	*High:* Carrion Crow, Jackdaw and Magpie common in diet

Table 8: (Continued)

Food type	Wales	Central England	Southern Spain	Germany
Pigeons	*Medium*	*High:* Mainly Woodpigeon, often taken as nestlings	*Low*	*High:* Mainly Domestic Pigeons, also Woodpigeon
Gamebirds	*Low*	*High:* Mostly full-grown Pheasants, also Red-legged Partridge	*Low*	*Medium:* Grey Partridge most common species; fewer Pheasants taken
Other birds	*Medium:* Low numbers of a wide variety of species	*Medium:* Low numbers of a wide variety of species	*Medium:* Low numbers of a wide variety of species	*High:* Domestic Fowl common in some areas; low numbers of a wide variety of other species
Amphibians and reptiles	*Medium:* Common Frog taken in small numbers	*Low*	*High:* Lizards and snakes fairly common in diet, frogs taken less frequently	*Low:* Lizards, snakes, frogs and toads all taken infrequently
Fish	*Low:* Remains of Brown Trout and Tench found at nest sites	*Low:* Freshwater fish remains found at nests, presumably carrion	*High:* Freshwater fish commonly taken, marine fish also recorded	*Medium:* Freshwater fish regular in some areas, very unusual in others
Invertebrates	*High:* Mainly earthworms and beetles; also other groups some probably ingested incidentally when feeding on larger prey	*Low/Medium:* Remains of earthworms in pellets found at nests	*Medium:* Commonly taken but making up only a small proportion of diet in terms of biomass	*Medium:* Study of single pair showed that earthworms and beetles can be important in early part of breeding season
Human waste/scraps	*High:* From slaughter houses, refuse tips and feeding stations	*Low/Medium:* Food increasingly provided by householders in gardens	*Medium*	*Medium:* Domestic Fowl and large mammals probably scavenged from waste disposal sites

carrion or was killed. It can be safely assumed that the larger mammals and birds were scavenged, as these species are simply too large and heavy for a Red Kite to kill and carry back to the nest. The breeding season is defined here as the period from nest-building through to independence of the young and varies slightly between the different areas.

The task of rearing young imposes certain restrictions on the type of prey taken, as food items for nestlings and, before the eggs have hatched, for the incubating female, must be carried to the nest site. Invertebrates are generally too small to be worthwhile for this purpose although earthworms are sometimes brought in and fed to chicks. At the other end of the scale, many animal carcasses are too heavy to be lifted. These food sources are still useful for the adult birds, particularly early in the season when they are not tied to the nest site, but, for the growing brood, prey of intermediate size is at a premium. Hille (1995b) carried out a detailed study of a single pair of Red Kites in the Rhön Biosphere Reserve in Germany, and found that invertebrates, particularly earthworms and beetles, were important foods for the adults early in the season. During March and April, when wet weather was frequent, the pair spent much time foraging on the ground for invertebrates. Later in the season, when the adults had young to feed, they spent more time searching for food on the wing and birds and mammals became much more important in the diet.

Small and medium-sized mammals and birds dominate the diet in Wales and England, and are also the most important groups in southern Spain. The Rabbit is the single most numerous species in the diet in these three areas and is also important in northern Scotland (Wildman *et al*. 1998) and, to a lesser extent, in southern Sweden (Kjellén 1996). The reduction in Rabbit numbers in the 1950s following the outbreak of myxomatosis is thought to have temporarily reduced breeding productivity in mid-Wales (Lovegrove *et al*. 1990). Just as Rabbit numbers in Spain were recovering from myxomatosis in the 1980s, viral haemorrhagic disease irrupted, reducing Rabbit populations in some areas by between one half and two thirds in the five years from 1988 to 1993. This initially provided an abundant source of carrion which may have benefited scavenging birds but, in the longer term, resulted in a substantial reduction in food availability (Viñuela & Villafuerte 2003).

In parts of Germany the Common Hamster is important in the diet, although populations of this prey species have declined as farming methods have become increasingly intensive. This species is an ideal prey in the breeding season as it provides a substantial meal but is still light enough to be carried back to the nest. The same applies to the similar-sized Brown Rat, which is frequently found at nest sites in England and Scotland. Feeding experiments carried out in the breeding season in southern England showed that small and medium-sized rat carcasses, up to about 150g, were favoured as food items as they could be picked up from the ground and carried away. The carcasses of large birds and rats of up to 450g could not be lifted and, as a result, were eaten far less frequently (Ntampakis 2003, Ntampakis & Carter 2005). Field Voles are the most important small mammal in the diet of Welsh birds and improved breeding success has been linked to years with high vole populations (Davis & Newton 1981). In southern Spain, Red Kites take significant amounts of reptiles and freshwater fish, each forming approximately 10% of the diet (Veiga & Hiraldo 1990). In southern Sweden, where birds are the most important group, 8% of the breeding season diet is made up of fish (Kjellén 1996).

Wales is the only place where carrion from large mammals is important during the breeding season. Davis and Davis (1981) found sheep remains in no less that 75% of pellets collected during the period from April to August. The proportion was highest in spring when pellets sometimes contained the small red rubber rings used to dock lambs' tails and scrota. Field observations showed that sheep placentas were also eaten. In contrast to more productive lowland areas, birds in parts of mid-Wales must rely heavily on sheep carrion, waste from slaughterhouses and, more recently, feeding stations, because there are limited alternative foods available.

Adult Red Kites carrying food back to nest sites often do so in as inconspic-uous a manner as possible, flying low down and with the talons tucked close in to the body, making small items of food very difficult to see. Viñuela (1992) has suggested that this is in order to minimise the risk of the food being seen and then stolen by other birds of prey, including other Red Kites, in the area.

Diet in the non-breeding season

Freed from the duties of provisioning young, Red Kites are able to exploit a far wider range of food-types outside the breeding season. Invertebrates are taken more frequently, and in Britain, earthworms are a particularly favoured food. Other types of invertebrate are taken frequently in some areas during the non-breeding season, including southern Spain, although they are thought to form only a very small proportion of the diet in terms of biomass.

Carrion from large mammals is important in winter in parts of Spain and in Sweden where Red Kites are also attracted to rubbish dumps to scavenge (Kjellén 1996). Sheep carrion continues to be important in Wales and meat provided at feeding stations supports large numbers of Red Kites through the cold winter months (see Chapter 7). In England and Scotland, carrion from large mammals is relatively unimportant. Livestock rearing is on a much smaller scale than in the uplands of mid-Wales and fewer carcasses become available in lowland areas where animals are kept in fields close to villages or farm buildings. There is also a greater abundance of carrion from smaller species that provide a more readily accessible source of food. Red Kites in England have only rarely been recorded visiting refuse tips although this habit appears to have increased in southern England in recent years. This may be a response to the increasing density of birds in some areas and a resulting decline in food availability, forcing birds to exploit alternative options.

In Germany, Ortlieb (1989) reported that birds overwintering in Baden-Württemburg fed almost exclusively on Common Voles and only very low numbers of other mammals, birds and invertebrates were recorded in the diet. In other parts of Germany, however, refuse tips are thought to provide an important source of food. On the northern plateau of central Spain, Common Voles can form up to 80% of the winter diet in vole plague years (Viñuela 1994) but livestock carrion is also important, particularly in years when vole numbers are low.

Feeding at animal carcasses

The Red Kite's lack of strength and relatively weak bill are a considerable disadvantage when it comes to tackling carcasses of larger mammals, as it is necessary to penetrate the tough outer skin in order to reach the meat beneath. In Wales, it is thought that sheep meat only becomes available to Red Kites once more powerful scavengers such as Foxes or Ravens have broken into the carcass, or after a certain amount of decomposition has taken place. The same may be true with large mammals in Spain, as groups of Red Kites have been repeatedly observed loafing in trees near to carcasses but not feeding. Garcìa et al. (1998) noted this behaviour and suggested that the birds were waiting for larger scavengers to open up carcasses before they could begin to feed. An alternative explanation is that these birds were reluctant to fly down to the carcass until they were sure that it was safe to do so. Such cautious behaviour is known to occur in African vultures, for example, where ground predators are a constant threat at carcasses. Large numbers of scavenging vultures may gather in trees near to a carcass before the bravest or, more likely, hungriest, fly down and begin to feed. Once a few birds have demonstrated that it is safe to feed, the rest quickly join in the feast (Snyder & Snyder 2000). Red Kites are often vocal when circling around a potential source of food and this may serve to attract other birds into the area so that the 'safety in numbers' effect is enhanced.

When individuals from several different species gather at a carcass, a dominance hierarchy is usually formed, determining which birds can feed first. This

Table 9: **Non-breeding season diet in Wales, England and Doñana National Park, southern Spain (Importance in diet ranked as *High, Medium* or *Low*)**

Information from Blanco et al. (1999a), Blanco et al. (1999b), Carter & Clarke (unpubl.), Davis & Davis (1981), Heredia et al. (1991)

Food type	Wales	Central England	Southern Spain
Large mammals	*High:* Dominated by sheep carrion, occasionally other wild and domestic animals	*Low:* Sheep and deer species infrequently taken	*Medium:* Both domestic and wild mammals
Lagomorph (Rabbits and hares)	*High:* Rabbits much more common in diet than Brown Hares	*High:* Mostly Rabbits, fewer Brown Hares	*High:* Rabbits and hares both commonly eaten
Brown Rat	*Medium*	*High:* Victims of poisoning campaigns are scavenged	*High*
Other small/medium-sized mammals	*High:* Including Field Vole, Mole and shrews	*High:* Small mammals, mainly Field Voles and Woodmouse; larger species including Weasel and Mole less common	*Medium:* Common Voles very common in diet in parts of Spain but less important in Doñana
Waterfowl	*Low*	*Low*	*High:* Greylag Goose carcasses an important food source; also other smaller species
Corvids	*Medium:* Including Jackdaw, Magpie, Carrion Crow, Rook and Jay	*Medium*	*Medium*

Table 9: **Non-breeding season diet in Wales, central England and Doñana National Park, southern Spain (Importance in diet ranked as *High, Medium* or *Low*)** *(continued)*
Information from Blanco et al. (1999a), Blanco et al. (1999b), Carter & Clarke (unpubl.), Davis & Davis (1981), Heredia et al. (1991)

Food type	Wales	Central England	Southern Spain
Gamebirds	*Low*	*High:* Mainly Pheasant, also Red-legged Partridge	*Low*
Other birds	*High:* Low numbers of a wide variety of species	*Medium:* Low numbers of a wide variety of species	*High:* Wide variety of different species
Amphibians and reptiles	*Low:* Common Frog taken infrequently	*Not recorded*	*Low*
Fish	*Low*	*Low:* Freshwater fish, presumably taken as carrion	*Low*
Invertebrates	*High:* Earthworms and beetles common in diet; wide range of other groups, some probably ingested incidentally when feeding on larger prey	*High:* Earthworms commonly taken; flying insects such as craneflies taken on the wing in late summer	*Medium:* Including ants, grasshoppers and beetles; common in diet but making up only small proportion of food in terms of biomass
Human waste/scraps	*High:* From slaughter houses, refuse tips and feeding stations	*Low/medium:* Only occasionally seen at refuse tips; food increasingly provided by householders in gardens	*Low:* But waste from livestock processing factories, refuse tips and livestock carcass dumps important in other parts of Spain

seems to vary greatly, depending on the situation and probably on the hunger of the birds involved, so that Red Kites are at times subordinate to Buzzards and Ravens but, on other occasions, can displace them from a carcass. When several Red Kites are present at a carcass they sometimes feed together without undue squabbling although, again, this varies depending on the situation. Hiraldo *et al.* (1991) found that in Doñana, southern Spain, Red Kites were most often seen at goose carcasses as single birds or small groups of up to four individuals. However, it was very unusual for more than a single bird to be actively feeding at the carcass at any one time.

Corvids, including Carrion Crows and Magpies, also regularly attend carcasses and, whilst they are subordinate to Red Kites, they can cause them no little irritation in their attempts to gain a share of the food. Magpies have even been watched apparently working as a team, with one bird hopping up behind a Red Kite and tugging at its tail feathers, while others take advantage of the distraction in order to steal food.

The importance of live prey versus carrion

It has been suggested by some authors that whilst Red Kites rely heavily on carrion during the winter, they take mostly live prey in the breeding season (e.g. Cramp & Simmons 1980, Davis & Davis 1981, Lovegrove 1990), although little evidence is provided to support this claim. Young, and therefore inexperienced, birds and mammals are available mainly in the summer and when their remains are found in pellets or at nest sites it is perhaps simply assumed that they are usually killed rather than taken as carrion.

Nevertheless, it is undoubtedly true that some live prey is taken. In Wales, Walters Davies and Davis (1973) found that some Red Kites visited Black-headed Gull colonies in order to take nestlings and, in one case, several rings that had been placed on gull chicks were found in pellets at a Red Kite nest 4km away from the gull colony. Steve Parr (reported by Lovegrove 1990) has seen Red Kites quartering low over woodland in what he interpreted as a systematic search for corvid or Woodpigeon nestlings, a behaviour that has also been recorded in southern England (Snell *et al.* 2002). In both England and Scotland, the partly-grown blood-feathers from nestling or recently fledged corvids and Woodpigeons are frequently found at nest sites. Some of the Woodpigeon remains have involved nestlings of pre-fledging age that presumably could have only been obtained direct from nests (Carter & Grice 2002). Taking such defenceless and immobile prey as nestlings can, in some ways, be seen as an extension of the bird's scavenging habits even though the prey is killed. Similar behaviour has been reported in other raptors that are not well known for killing their prey.

Roberts *et al.* (1999) noted that Woodpigeon and Turtle Dove squabs were sometimes taken by Honey Buzzards, in contrast to their staple diet of wasp larvae, and Griffon Vultures have been recorded taking the chicks of White Storks from their nests (Berlijn 2003).

In March at a site in Germany, a Red Kite was watched flying above a lake, struggling with a large fish, the observer having been alerted by the sound of a loud splash. There was no doubt that the fish was taken as live prey as it could be seen wriggling wildly in the bird's talons (Crease 1998). This is one of a number of reports of Red Kites taking fish from lakes although it is often unclear as to whether they have been taken live or scavenged.

Intensive studies involving prolonged observations of foraging Red Kites tend to confirm that killing of live prey is relatively unusual. In central England, during many hundreds of hours of observations aided by radio-tracking, only a single example of active hunting for live prey (other than for invertebrates) was witnessed. This involved a bird flying low over the ground and then dropping, with talons outstretched, into long grass, probably in an attempt to catch a small mammal. In Wales, Davis and Davis (1981) recorded such behaviour in every month from June to December and reported a small number of successful attacks on full-grown birds up to the size of a Rook. Active hunting has also been observed on a number of occasions by those monitoring the reintroduced Red Kites in northern Scotland (Wildman *et al.* 1998).

It seems likely that carrion is the preferred source of food and, where readily available, in a form suitable for carrying back to the nest, it makes up the bulk of the diet in the breeding season as well as in winter. In areas where carrion is in short supply, or where a pair learns to exploit a source of easily caught live prey, active hunting may become more important.

Remains of nestlings or recently fledged young of birds such as Woodpigeon (right), Carrion Crow and Black-headed Gull are regularly found at Red Kite nests in Britain (Ian Carter)

Prey specialisation

Studies of food remains or pellets found at Red Kite nest sites usually reveal a highly varied diet, as indicated in the tables above. At some nests, however, the remains are dominated by a particular food-type, upon which the pair has clearly learnt to specialise. Walters Davies and Davis (1973) found nests where the food remains consisted mainly of Black-headed Gulls, Magpies or Jackdaws, in each case with relatively few other species present. Hen Pheasants dominated the food remains at one nest in central England, situated only 1km away from a Pheasant laying pen. The local gamekeeper witnessed adult Red Kites removing dead birds from within the pen, noting that they could carry away the carcasses only because the birds had died from a wasting disease and were far lighter than usual. At a nest just over 1km away from this pair, 71% of pellets contained pigeon remains, and feathers found below the nest suggested that this pair were specialising on young Woodpigeons (Carter & Grice 2002). The remains of 17 Moles were found in a single visit to a nest site in central Scotland (Duncan Orr-Ewing pers. comm.) suggesting an element of specialisation although, interestingly, all were either intact or had only their heads missing. Uneaten Moles have also been found at other nests in Britain, as well as at Buzzard nests (Tubbs 1974), suggesting that this species is rather unpalatable. That they are sometimes consumed has been confirmed by finding Mole fur in a small number of pellets in England (Carter & Grice 2002).

Walters Davies and Davis (1973) suggested that food specialisation might also occur outside the breeding season, noting that the proportions of different food-types varied greatly in collections of winter pellets from different communal roosts within the same area. They also believed that certain individual Red Kites frequently foraged for invertebrates at particular locations whilst others in the same area, and with the same opportunities, seldom did so.

Chapter 7

HABITATS AND LAND-USE

Climate and relief

The Red Kite is a generalist and adaptable species and its basic requirements are met by a wide range of different landscape types and climatic conditions across its European range. Nevertheless, it does have certain preferences, and these are reflected in its pattern of distribution. As a general rule, extremes of climate are not favoured and so areas with either excessively hot and dry, or cool and damp, conditions are often avoided. Currently, Red Kites breed no further north in Europe than Denmark and southern Sweden, and there is a clear tendency to avoid the damper conditions on the north-western fringe of Europe (see map in Chapter 3). The species is, for example, absent from north-western parts of Spain and France, where a damp Atlantic climate prevails (Viñuela 1994), and, in similar conditions in central Wales, the population suffers from poor breeding productivity and has taken a long time to recover from past persecution. At the other end of the climatic extreme, the breeding range does not extend into the arid conditions found in North Africa and the Middle East (with the possible exception of a small remnant population in Morocco) and Red Kite breeding productivity in the lowlands of southern Europe tends to be much lower than in populations further north (Mougeot & Bretagnolle 2006, see Chapter 8). In Spain, there are few Red Kites in the areas with the hottest and driest conditions in summer, such as the Mediterranean coast and much of the south and east of the country (Viñuela 1994, Seoane et al. 2003).

The reasons for avoiding these extremes of climate probably involve both direct effects on breeding productivity, through reductions in hatching success and survival rates of chicks, and indirect effects through a reduction in food availability. Cool and damp conditions may reduce hatching success and certainly increase mortality rates of small chicks while they are still covered with down (Cross & Davis 2005). The effect of poor weather on food availability is thought to reduce breeding productivity in Wales. Cool, wet weather restricts the ability of the adults to forage for food, thus compounding the effects of lower prey densities. Newton et al. (1981) found that, at higher altitudes in mid-Wales, egg-laying was slightly later, on average, and a smaller proportion of nests produced young than with nests on lower ground. It is also likely that very hot conditions have an adverse effect on Red Kites, again, either directly due to the adverse effects of high temperatures on eggs and chicks, or through a reduction in the availability of suitable food. As well as influencing general patterns of distribution, climatic conditions also influence seasonal movements. Many pairs breeding in upland areas, for example, move onto lower ground in winter to escape the harsh weather found more frequently at higher altitudes. Areas of the breeding range with severe conditions in winter, such as central and eastern Europe, support far fewer birds at this time of year (Chapter 4).

The Red Kite is not a common breeder above about 1,000m in southern Europe, although there are some records of birds breeding at higher altitudes, including at up to 2,500m in Morocco (Ferguson-Lees & Christie 2001). In central and northern Europe, breeding is very uncommon at altitudes greater than 600m (Viñuela 1994, Snow & Perrins 1998). The avoidance of these more mountainous areas is no doubt strongly linked to the climatic factors discussed above, as a wet and cool climate is more likely at higher altitudes. On a more local scale, Red Kites tend to select areas with undulating topography so that they can utilise the rising air currents that result from wind deflected by sloping ground. Flat areas are not entirely unsuitable as lift for foraging flights can be derived from thermals in sunny weather but, in many areas, a distinct preference for foothills and the lower mountain slopes is apparent and flat, open plains are used less frequently (Seoane *et al*. 2003). It has been suggested that, in Spain, this preference might also be the result of a partial ecological separation between the Red and Black Kite, two species with a considerable overlap in diet (Heredia *et al*. 1991, Viñuela *et al*. 1999). Black Kites are often abundant on lower ground, breeding successfully in very hot areas, but become less frequent in the foothills where the climate is cooler, and this perhaps allows these areas to support higher densities of Red Kites due to reduced competition for food and nest sites. Some lowland areas with abundant Black Kites support few Red Kites in summer, but become important for the species in winter, when there is no competition from the migratory Black Kite.

In Britain, the Red Kite is currently present in only small areas of its potential range but is expected to spread to new areas as the Welsh and reintroduced populations continue to expand. Even in the cool, damp, upland areas of mid-Wales, the species has managed to survive and increase slowly although it is clear that conditions here are far from ideal. Elsewhere in Britain, the only areas likely to be unsuitable for Red Kites are the highest parts of the Pennines, Cumbrian mountains and the Highlands of Scotland, and perhaps also the largely treeless flatlands of the East Anglian fens. Even these areas might be capable of supporting low densities of birds and, in the uplands, all but the highest ground may be utilised in summer by foraging birds.

Land management and human activities

The Red Kite, as with many other predominantly open-country birds, has benefited greatly from the mixed landscape created by humans, and it would not have been a common bird when Europe was mainly covered in natural forest. Although the majority of foraging is carried out over open countryside, where the Red Kite can make best use of its superb eyesight to detect potential sources of food, woodland is also an important component of the landscape. Patches of woodland not only provide sites for roosting and nesting, but are also utilised by many of the species most frequent in the Red Kite's diet. In Britain, the Rabbit is one of the most important species in the diet throughout the year and is often most numerous on the boundaries between woodland or scrub and open fields. Woodpigeons, Pheasants and corvids are also frequent in the diet and all require woodland for nesting, roosting and shelter. For similar reasons, wetlands are important in parts of the Red Kite's range as they tend to support a high diversity of potential prey, often in an open environment where food is readily detectable.

With the possible exception of its close relative, the Black Kite, the Red Kite is more closely associated with human activities in the countryside than any other bird of prey in Europe. The bird's comparative lack of fear of humans allows it to take advantage of feeding opportunities created as farming operations are carried out, and also means that food sources close to human habitation are exploited. As a result, the Red Kite is a species with which local people often become familiar in the areas where it occurs. The rest of this chapter concentrates on the association between the Red Kite and human activities and helps to explain why it is able to thrive in such a diversity of different landscapes, provided that it is not persecuted.

Forestry

As described above, a certain amount of forest cover is an important part of the landscape for Red Kites as it provides nesting and roosting areas, together with habitat for some of the species most important in the diet. Only relatively small patches of woodland are required for breeding sites and communal roosts and, with the exception of clear-fells and newly planted areas, foraging is carried out over unforested open ground. It is therefore easy to see that, above a certain threshold level, forest cover may become detrimental to Red Kites, restricting the area available for foraging and therefore limiting the number of birds that an area is able to support.

Afforestation has long been a concern in central Wales, as it was feared that the loss of upland sheep grazing would reduce foraging opportunities for Red Kites and lead to reductions in survival and breeding productivity. From the early 1960s there was a major expansion of afforestation schemes, encouraged by Government incentives to boost timber production in Britain. As a result, more than 25% of the Welsh uplands has been covered with commercial coniferous forest. Research has been undertaken in Wales specifically to find out whether this increase in forest cover has had an adverse effect on the local Red Kites (Newton et al. 1996). This work showed that, despite the loss of a few breeding territories as a result of afforestation, overall, there was no noticeable negative effect on distribution or breeding productivity. In fact, in the first 12-15 years, newly planted areas with only small trees and plenty of rough grassland, support high densities of voles, an important food source for Red Kites. It was also suspected that increased afforestation led to a drop in incidents of illegal poisoning as this practice is carried out mainly by sheep farmers trying to protect livestock on upland grazing land. Despite these findings, there is no doubt that mature conifer plantations do not provide suitable foraging areas and so, above a certain level, afforestation is likely to have an adverse effect on Red Kites. In Wales, where the population is still recovering from past persecution, breeding densities may not yet have reached the level at which a reduction in the available foraging area has a noticeable effect.

Arable farmland

Landscapes dominated by intensively managed arable farmland are not ideal for Red Kites as the densities of most potential prey species will be relatively low on land that is cultivated on a regular basis and subject to routine pesticide treatment. However, areas where this land-use predominates are not avoided completely, as long as there is at least some variation in the landscape. Alternative habitats are particularly important in the latter part of the breeding season when arable crops are well grown, as Red Kites are reluctant to land in thick vegetation and food on the ground is difficult to detect when obscured by dense crops. Arable farmland is used much more frequently in autumn and winter and, in Spain, extensive, virtually treeless, expanses of arable farmland support large numbers of wintering Red Kites (García et al. 1998).

In central England, observations of birds in autumn and winter showed that although grassland was the most preferred habitat, arable fields were utilised in roughly the same proportion as they were present in the study area (Table 10). The same pattern was apparent when only observations of feeding birds were included, showing that arable fields do provide foraging habitat at this time of year (Carter & Grice 2002). In the Chiltern Hills, southern England, Dixon (2001) found a similar pattern in winter with 'meadow' and 'pasture' preferred but arable fields utilised regularly. Observations of foraging birds show that invertebrates, especially earthworms, are obtained from bare arable fields as well as small mammals that may have been killed during recent agricultural operations.

In eastern Germany, an increase in intensive arable farming has been blamed for local declines in breeding Red Kite populations and a lowering of productivity in areas supporting high population densities (George 1995). Here, there has been a decline in grassland and alfalfa (lucerne), managed for the production

Table 10: **Land-use categories utilised by Red Kites in central England, September-February, 1995-99** *(Carter & Grice 2000)*

Land-use	Percentage land-use class in study area[1]	Percentage (number) of Red Kite observations
Arable farmland	60	62 (255)
Grassland	20	26 (107)
Woodland	15	11 (45)
Other land (including built environment and open water)	5	1 (4)

[1]Information on land-use from ordnance survey maps and Government farm census data

of livestock fodder, and a shift to the cultivation of maize, following the reunification of Germany and the subsequent influence of the European Union's Common Agricultural Policy. The landscape here is still capable of supporting a reasonable density of Red Kites but apparently not the very high densities that were present when farmland was managed less intensively and food was more abundant throughout the breeding season.

As a result of production surpluses of many arable crops, and the huge burden of agricultural subsidies on European Union budgets, there has been increasing pressure for a switch to more environmentally friendly methods of farming. This has already led to a more varied landscape in predominantly arable areas with the introduction of statutory set-aside, where fields are left uncultivated for a year or more, and schemes such as Environmental Stewardship in England, with payments available for a range of measures aimed at encouraging wildlife. A popular option is to leave margins around the edges of cultivated fields, where pesticides and herbicides are not used. These strips support a greater diversity and density of arable weeds than the main crop, which, in turn, attracts invertebrates and provides a food source for a variety of birds and mammals. Uncultivated field margins also provide greater opportunities for nesting birds, many of which would struggle to survive within the cultivated crop. As the Red Kite has such a varied diet, all such measures that increase the overall diversity and abundance of wildlife in cultivated areas, are likely to be of considerable benefit.

Agricultural operations

It is well known that a variety of bird species have learnt to exploit feeding opportunities provided by routine farming activities. Village (1990), for example, described how Kestrels took advantage of crop harvesting in order to prey on small mammals, an apparently regular occurrence in the fens of eastern England where sugar-beet and potato-harvesting machinery is followed and the mammals taken as they are disturbed by the machines. Image (1992) recorded Montagu's Harriers following farm machinery in eastern England and thought that they were taking small mammals or the chicks of ground-nesting birds. Flocks of gulls following the plough are a far more familiar sight and, in this case, it is earthworms and other invertebrates that are taken as they are exposed by the action of the plough. Red Kites regularly feed on both small mammals and invertebrates, and they too take advantage of agricultural operations where these make food more easily accessible.

Farmers in central England frequently see Red Kites when they are working in the fields, and often remark on how close the birds come to their tractor or combine harvester. Red Kites are also observed foraging in fields where farming activities have taken place within the past few days, including stubble fields following harvest, grass fields cut for silage, and recently ploughed fields. It is usually impossible to see what the birds are feeding on in these situations but the food items picked up are almost always very small and could well include invertebrates and small mammals exposed by farm machinery. This may explain the high numbers of the normally nocturnal Woodmouse found in Red Kite pellets in autumn and winter in central England. This species is common in crop fields and many are probably killed or injured when ploughing destroys their burrows. In mid-Wales, Walters Davies and Davis (1973) reported that Red Kites took both invertebrates and small mammals after grass fields were cut for hay and suggested that some of the small mammals were likely to have been killed or injured during the cutting process. Red Kites regularly follow farm machinery in northern Scotland and have become a very familiar sight to some tractor drivers. Brian Etheridge has described two activities that are particularly attractive to foraging birds – the spring ploughing of winter stubble and the cutting of hayfields in late summer. One of his observations involved several Red Kites swooping down to the ground behind a tractor, almost lost to view amongst a swirling flock of Black-headed and Common Gulls.

Records of birds following farm machinery are also frequent on the continent. Single Black and Red Kites were seen to follow a mowing machine as it cut a hayfield in the Auvergne, France, with both birds making regular stoops to the ground as if picking up food items (Warren 1989). In Germany, Ortlieb (1989) reported that Red Kites and Buzzards often take small mammals disturbed when arable fields are ploughed. A photograph in his book *Der Rotmilan* (The Red Kite) shows two Red Kites circling directly above a tractor as it ploughs a field, and a Buzzard standing on a recently ploughed part of the same field. In Spain, groups of as many as 70 birds have been seen foraging in association with farm machinery as a field is ploughed. Viñuela (1992) thought that these birds were probably taking advantage of Common Voles, killed, or forced out into the open, as their burrows were destroyed. Hille (1995b) recorded details of foraging flights over various habitats in the Rhön Biosphere Reserve in Germany during spring and summer in 1994. She found that foraging birds were most successful in locating food when flying over meadows where farming operations (hay cut, turned or collected) had been carried out in the previous 1-2 days.

Livestock farming

Farmland managed primarily for livestock is one of the most important habitats for Red Kites throughout the year. In regions where livestock is reared extensively, being left to roam over large areas of relatively poor quality grazing, the animals themselves become an important source of food. This has long been the case in mid-Wales where sheep grazing is the major land-use. Sheep carrion is taken by Red Kites throughout the year but is particularly important in late winter, when the mortality of adult ewes reaches a peak, and in spring during the lambing season. Davis and Davis (1981) referred to the period between late autumn and early spring as the 'hungry gap' when other sources of food are scarce in the unproductive landscape of central Wales. Sheep carrion helps to bridge this gap, providing a valuable source of food that, as a result of increased sheep mortality, is more abundant when weather conditions are at their worst and extra food is most needed.

Over the last few decades, large areas of the Welsh uplands have been fenced off and are now managed as improved pasture. These areas still provide some sheep carrion in winter and at lambing time, and they are also much used by Red Kites hunting for invertebrates, particularly earthworms during wet weather. They are seen as visually intrusive by some, as the fields replace semi-natural areas of moorland and the bright green, artificial, swards stand out sharply in the upland landscape. However, because of the relative abundance of invertebrates in these heavily manured pastures and the resulting increases in birds and mammals that prey on them, they have probably been an overall benefit to the Red Kite (Lovegrove 1990).

In Spain, Viñuela (1993) found that Red Kites were often associated with cattle rearing areas in the breeding season, and with pig and chicken farms throughout the year. This was thought to be mainly because of the overall abundance of potential prey in these areas rather than a direct result of the presence of livestock. In the cattle-rearing areas, for example, rodents and small birds such as Starlings were common, attracted by the high numbers of invertebrates able to thrive in the dung-enriched pastures. Livestock carrion is an additional source of food in these areas, mainly in winter when other prey species are less easy to come by.

Regions where fighting bulls are reared provide some of the best areas for breeding Red Kites in Spain. These areas are relatively undisturbed, as, for obvious reasons, few people are inclined to wander over the fields where the bulls are grazing. As a result, there is usually little or no hunting activity and so levels of persecution are likely to be low. A rather more unexpected reason why livestock areas may be preferred in the breeding season is the use of sheep's wool and, in parts of Spain, cattle dung as a nest building material (Viñuela 1993). However, not all pairs use this material, so it is unlikely to be an important factor in determining local breeding densities.

The disposal of dead livestock on open dumps, referred to as 'middens' in Scotland, and, in Spain, as 'muladares' (mule dumps), provides sites where Red Kites can gain access to a predictable source of food in the form of animal carrion. The degree to which such sites are used depends on the availability of alternative foods but it is known that, in some areas, they can be very important, particularly in winter. A study in north-eastern Spain found that carrion from domestic animals made up between 39 and 54% of the diet for wintering birds at three different communal roosts (Larraz 1999). In addition, García et al. (1998) found that the proportion of chicken remains found in pellets was positively related to the density of chicken farms with 10km of communal roosts. In central and northern Europe, livestock carrion can also be important for birds that remain during the winter, particularly in years when alternative prey, such as voles, is not abundant.

Abattoirs, rubbish tips and factories where livestock carcasses are processed also provide sites where waste products form a predictable food supply. In Wales, small slaughter-houses were formerly much used by Red Kites in winter, but stricter European Union regulations governing these facilities has meant that many have long-since closed down (Davis & Davis 1981). In Spain, meat factories that process pigs, sheep and cattle often produce considerable waste such as intestines and other less valuable parts of the carcass, and are much frequented by scavengers. For example, a refuse tip in Cantimpalos, where slaughter-house remains were common, attracted a feeding concentration of up to 300 Red Kites (García et al. 1998).

There has been a great deal of concern about the effects that tighter EU regulations relating to the disposal of animal carcasses are having on scavenging birds of prey. It is now illegal in EU countries to leave livestock carcasses in the open countryside and they must, instead, be burnt, buried or dumped at specially built sites which may be more difficult to access by aerial scavengers. In areas where this legislation is strictly enforced, there are likely to be adverse effects on scavengers, particularly the larger vulture species in southern Europe, for which the carcasses of larger mammals form the bulk of the diet. Bearded, Griffon, Black and Egyptian Vultures are all listed as Species of European Conservation Concern and, although they are now increasing following past reductions due to persecution, the decrease in the availability of carrion from large domestic animals may be restricting rates of expansion and population densities (Tucker & Heath 1994). Red Kites are unlikely to be as seriously affected as the vultures, as they are less dependent on large carcasses, but there may still be local effects if this type of food becomes less easily available in future.

Feeding stations and hand-outs

The deliberate provision of food for scavenging birds of prey, in ways that conform to the legislation on disposal of livestock, should go some way to compensating for the loss of carcasses in the open countryside. Feeding stations have long been used as a conservation tool for supporting vulture populations in several southern European countries, particularly in areas where reintroduction projects have been carried out. In Scotland and Wales, several feeding stations aimed primarily at Red Kites have now been established, including the well-known centre at Gigrin Farm, near Rhayader in mid-Wales. At this site, pieces of meat small enough to be snatched up from the ground are put out at the same time each day throughout the year. Specially-built hides allow visitors to watch the spectacular display at close range. Up to 400 birds have been attracted to a single feeding session in winter, perhaps the largest feeding concentration of Red Kites that has been recorded in modern times. The meat is of a quality fit for human consumption so that animal health regulations are not infringed.

On a more local scale, householders in parts of Britain have managed to entice Red Kites into gardens in villages and the edges of small towns by providing food scraps on a regular basis. One person in southern England told a reporter from the *Sunday Telegraph* (17 May 1998) that he provided chicken scraps and dead mice on the back lawn and described how the Red Kites flew in 'like Stuka bombers' to snatch up and fly off with the food. Cameras at nest sites have recorded adult birds bringing in meat scraps and even a chicken drumstick at one nest in the Chilterns. At least one local butcher has taken to selling unwanted offcuts of meat as 'kite-scraps'. Some people dislike the idea of feeding Red Kites, seeing it as unnatural and likely to change the patterns of behaviour of foraging birds by encouraging large numbers into a relatively small area. There is also a concern that feeding could slow down the rate at which the population is able to spread to suitable countryside in new areas. It is certainly true that the reintroduced populations have been slow to spread out and recolonise suitable countryside well away from the release sites but this is, at least in part, the result of the bird's inherently social nature and high levels of natal philopatry (Chapter 9).

There are also some practical problems with providing food for Red Kites. There is the risk that food could attract other, less welcome, scavengers including rats and corvids, and that food such as cooked or processed meat could have adverse effects on the health of the birds that feed on it. Red Kites derive valuable nutrients from the skin and small bones of animal carcasses that are not present in scraps of meat provided by householders (see Chapter 11 for possible effects). It is also possible that additives such as salt in processed meat could have harmful effects. In order to address these concerns in the Chilterns, where feeding has become commonplace, some simple guidelines have been developed by organisations involved in Red Kite conservation (see text box for summary).

Feeding guidelines for Red Kites in the Chilterns

- In productive lowland areas where they have been reintroduced, natural food is plentiful and Red Kites do not need artificial food sources in order to thrive

- Artificial food based on meat that has been processed for human consumption may contain harmful additives such as salt

- Food provided should preferably be derived from complete animal carcasses, including skin and bone, so that beneficial nutrients and minerals are present

- Food should be cleared up at the end of each day to avoid attracting pests

- Neighbours should be consulted and any concerns they have should be taken into account before food is provided

---

It is worth remembering that Red Kites have always taken advantage of food scraps resulting from human activities, including, as far back as medieval times, within our towns and cities. Provided that simple guidelines are followed, the deliberate feeding of Red Kites is unlikely to cause serious problems and is perhaps little different to the widespread practice of providing food for a wide range of species at bird tables which is now such a common occurrence. In areas such as central Wales, where natural foods can be hard to come by, organised feeding is likely to be a substantial benefit to the local Red Kite population.

Game rearing

In parts of lowland Britain, large numbers of gamebirds (mainly Pheasants and Red-legged Partridges) are reared and released in huge numbers in order to provide a surplus for the shooting season. Densities are extremely high in some areas, which, in turn, can lead to high levels of mortality, and provide a valuable source of carrion for the Red Kite. The number of Pheasants that can be seen dead on roads in many areas provides a good indication of the scale of the food resource available.

The management of Pheasants on shooting estates involves the use of large, open-topped pens where the laying females are kept so that their eggs can be collected and incubated artificially. The chicks are then reared indoors before being placed in open-topped release pens where food is provided and where they can gradually adapt to life in the wild. Red Kites in some areas have learnt that both laying pens and release pens are a likely source of dead birds and gamekeepers in England frequently see them flying low overhead or even diving down into a pen to retrieve a carcass. A Pheasant carcass would normally be too heavy for a Red Kite to carry but those that die as a result of disease are often in poor condition and are therefore light enough to be taken back to the nest.

Throughout the autumn and winter shooting season, large numbers of gamebirds are killed as birds are driven by beaters over lines of guns. Most of the dead birds are picked up by gun-dogs but, inevitably, not all are retrieved and those that are missed become available to scavengers. Birds that are 'pricked' by pellets from a shotgun, but not killed outright, may die later, providing a further source of carrion. Some gamekeepers in England have reported that Red Kites appear in an area as soon as the shooting starts, as if they have learnt to

associate the noise of gunfire with the chance of obtaining food. If these reports are anything other than coincidence, such behaviour offers a welcome contrast to the times, not so long ago, when game-rearing estates would have been very dangerous places for a Red Kite to search for food.

Estates where shooting is important will tend to be managed in a way that encourages gamebirds. This may include leaving field margins uncultivated, maintaining a high density of hedgerows in order to provide nest sites, and retaining areas of woodland for shelter and to provide flushing points so that birds can be driven over the guns. This sort of management encourages a diversity of other wildlife, including species such as Rabbit, Brown Hare, small mammals and birds that make up a significant part of the Red Kite's diet. Some species also benefit from the grain feeding stations and strips of game cover crop provided by gamekeepers to reduce the chance that gamebirds will stray away from the estate. Whatever the moral objections some people have to the shooting of birds for sport, there is no doubt that shooting estates offer considerable opportunities to a whole range of wildlife, including the Red Kite.

Pest control

Farmers and gamekeepers frequently undertake pest control programmes in order to protect gamebirds, livestock or crops, and this provides another regular food source for the adaptable Red Kite. Rabbits are almost universally disliked by farmers and are controlled by trapping or night shooting with a rifle and high-powered lamp. When large numbers are shot they are frequently left where they fall, as carcasses have little commercial value, and it is time consuming to collect them. Sometimes they are deliberately left as food for Foxes in order to reduce the chance of predation of livestock or gamebirds, and some farmers now leave them specifically in order to feed the local Red Kites.

Another regular target for pest control is the Brown Rat, especially on arable farms where grain and game cover crops provide them with an abundant food supply. They may be trapped, shot or gassed but poisoning is by far the most frequently used method of control. The most commonly used poisons are based on anticoagulants and take several days to work effectively. As a result, animals may die some distance from where the bait was eaten and even individuals poisoned inside farm buildings can become available to scavengers if they die outside. Brown Rats form an important part of the Red Kite's diet in many areas but, where poisoned animals are taken, there is the very real risk of secondary poisoning, a subject that is dealt with in Chapter 11.

Other species regularly controlled by gamekeepers, farmers and foresters include Stoat, Weasel, Mink, Grey Squirrel, Woodpigeon and several members of the corvid family. Trapping is the main method of control for most of the mammals and corvids and so carcasses only become available to Red Kites if the individual checking the trap deliberately leaves them out in the open. Woodpigeons, however, are often shot as they fly in to feeding or roosting areas and are not always collected for human consumption.

Road-kills

This is yet another example of how the Red Kite is able to take advantage of a source of food that has only become available in relatively recent times, as a direct result of one of our major impacts on the environment. It is now difficult to travel more than a few hundred metres on any busy road without seeing the evidence of birds and mammals killed by passing vehicles. Marchant and Gregory (1999) suggested that rising traffic densities and the resultant increase in road-kills could help to explain increases in the numbers of Rooks and other scavenging corvids in Britain. The Red Kite, being a carrion specialist, undoubtedly also benefits from this source of food.

Corvids, especially Rooks, Carrion Crows and Magpies, have become adept at exploiting road casualties, taking advantage of even small gaps in the traffic on our busiest roads and motorways in order to feed. Red Kites are much more hesitant in such situations and are only infrequently witnessed scavenging on road-kills. They probably only visit the busier roads in early morning when there is little traffic. Smaller carcasses may be picked up and carried to a nearby field or tree where they can be eaten in safety, but Red Kites will, on occasion,

feed at the roadside, usually after first circling in ever tighter circles to make sure that the coast is clear. Evidence that Red Kites take road casualties comes not only from direct observations but also from studies of food remains. In England, bird carcasses found at nest sites sometimes have a broken wing, most likely sustained when hit by a vehicle, and some mammal carcasses retrieved from nests are squashed almost flat as a result of passing vehicles, before they were retrieved as food.

Viñuela (1997) was concerned that a census of Red Kites in Spain carried out using road-transect counts could overestimate the population because birds were specifically attracted to roads in order to scavenge. The problem was most apparent in northern Spain where Red Kites were not only attracted by road-kills but also by the high numbers of voles inhabiting roadside ditches.

Many species probably only become available to foraging Red Kites when killed by vehicles as they are unlikely to be taken as live prey and deaths from natural causes normally occur in thick cover where the carcasses are inaccessible. In Britain, examples include Moorhen, Little Owl and Hedgehog. All three have been found as food remains at nest sites and, as a result of their behaviour, all are regular victims on our roads.

Chapter 8

THE BREEDING SEASON

In parts of Europe where the Red Kite is not migratory, many established breeding pairs stay together during the winter, spending much time close to their nest site. Some pairs, particularly those on higher ground, where food is not always easy to come by, leave the breeding area and range more widely, perhaps taking advantage of refuse tips or a winter feeding station. Most of these pairs will have returned to their breeding sites by late February and, in Britain, most of the activity relating to territory establishment takes place during March when breeding pairs are often very conspicuous near to the nest site. By early April, most nests have been built or refurbished ready for laying.

The season begins slightly later in the mainly migratory populations in central and northern Europe where most adults return to their breeding sites during March.

Age of first breeding

In areas providing ideal habitat in England and Scotland, most Red Kites breed for the first time when they are two years old. In England this is almost always the case and birds probably only delay breeding beyond this time if, as a result of a local imbalance in the sexes, for example, they are unable to find a mate. In Scotland, most birds also begin breeding when two years old but some, mainly males, make their first attempt when in their third or even fourth year (Evans *et al.* 1999). In central Scotland, Orr-Ewing *et al.* (2006) found that 70% of released birds bred for the first time when two years old, with the remaining 30% of birds making their first attempt at three years of age. In Wales, there is a significantly greater spread in age of first breeding. Studies of wing-tagged birds have shown that many do not breed until their third or fourth year and some are not recorded breeding for the first time until they are as old as seven (Newton *et al.* 1989, Cross & Davis 1998). This difference reflects the less than ideal habitat and lower food availability in mid-Wales. Red Kites find it more difficult to get into breeding condition when conditions are less suitable and may only achieve this when they are older and more experienced.

First-year birds sometimes pair up and hold territory, and may even construct a nest. By doing so they gain valuable experience for the following year when they have a much higher chance of success. Reintroduced birds in England and Scotland have occasionally bred successfully in their first year, the first time this has been recorded in Red Kites. The handful of cases have mainly involved a first-year bird paired with an older bird, but there have been at least two pairs in England involving a male and female, both only one year old. This was first recorded in southern England where a first-year pair successfully reared a single chick. Analysis of DNA from blood samples was used to confirm that the two first-year birds holding territory were indeed the true parents of the chick (Evans *et al.* 1998). Remarkably, a male bird released in Yorkshire in 1999 became a 'grandfather' at just two years of age. This individual bred in its first year, with one of its offspring then going on to breed successfully in the following year (Doug Simpson pers. comm.).

By studying individually-marked reintroduced birds in Britain, Evans *et al.* (1999) showed that breeding productivity improved as birds became more experienced during their first 3-4 years of life. A total of 72 birds breeding as two-year-olds reared, on average, 1.6 young per breeding attempt, whereas 88 more experienced birds, aged three years or more, reared an average of 2.3 young per breeding attempt. It has also been shown in Wales that both clutch size and breeding productivity tend to increase with age. Davis *et al.* (2001) found that, for both sexes, the production of fledged young was, on average, almost twice as great for three-year-old birds than for birds breeding at two years, mainly due to a lower proportion of breeding failures. In females, productivity continued to increase up to at least the fifth year.

The breeding pair and site faithfulness

Red Kites are, in some ways, rather similar to humans in their mating strategy. Once paired, they usually remain together until the death of one of the pair, but, occasionally, 'divorces' are recorded. This is most likely to occur when a breeding pair fails to rear any young. If one member of the pair then has the opportunity to join up with a more successful bird then it may do so in order to improve its chances of breeding successfully in the following season. Davis *et al.* (2001) list several examples of divorce based on observations of wing-tagged birds in Wales, all involving inexperienced birds which divorced after making their first breeding attempt.

Studies of individually-marked birds have revealed a behaviour that is rather less frequent in humans – the pairing of very closely related individuals. This occurred in 1997-2000 in northern Scotland when a brother and sister, reared at the same nest in 1995, paired up and reared a total of seven young in four successful nesting attempts. There has also been a father-daughter pairing in the same area (Brian Etheridge pers. comm.). Davis *et al.* (2001) noted several examples in Wales including two brother-sister pairings and one between mother and son. Pairing between brother and sister has also been recorded in southern England (Dixon 2001). Such incestuous pairings may result from the fact that young birds often return to their natal area to breed and are therefore quite likely to come into contact with their parents or siblings. It is unlikely that individuals are able to recognise close relatives when they come across them later in life (see under 'Fledging to independence' later in chapter) and so, despite the possible genetic disadvantages of inbreeding, a small proportion of these pairs arise purely by chance.

There have been instances where a third Red Kite present in an occupied territory during the breeding season, has apparently been tolerated by the resident pair (Walters Davies & Davis 1973, Davis *et al.* 2001). One two-year-old female even brooded the small young of an established pair at a Welsh nest. These birds have sometimes been referred to as 'aunties', and it has been suggested that they are tolerated because they are closely related to the breeding pair. However, observations of wing-tagged birds have now shown that third birds in a territory are sometimes not close relatives of the breeding pair. In cases where third birds are related this may simply reflect the fact that young birds often return to close to their natal site in the first or second summer after fledging. In northern Scotland, for example, there have been two reported instances where young females, fledged in the previous year, were present close to the nest of the established pair during the following breeding season (Brian Etheridge pers. comm.). It is unclear what these birds hope to gain from spending time in another pair's territory but perhaps they derive some experience of breeding behaviour which could be useful when they come to breed for themselves.

Van Kleef and Bustamante (1999) recorded the first ever example of polygamous mating in the Red Kite in Doñana National Park, southern Spain in 1997. A single male, identifiable by its colour ring, helped two different females to build nests about 750m apart and was seen mating with both. The male then assisted just one of the females in providing food for her young but, despite this, both nests were successful in producing at least one fledgling. Apparent polygamy has also been recorded in the reintroduced population in Dumfries and Galloway in southern Scotland, although neither of the females involved produced young. This behaviour is difficult to detect without intensive monitoring of individually-marked birds and it may well occur more regularly than is suggested by the small number of cases reported.

Breeding pairs tend to remain faithful to a particular territory, returning year after year to breed at the same site. Pairs do sometimes move to an alternative breeding site, but this is usually within 10km, and often much closer. Once a territory has been established it will frequently remain in use for many years, even if something happens to the initial pair. One such traditional site in mid-Wales was used continuously for at least 17 years, and some Welsh sites, known to be occupied over 100 years ago, are still in use in modern times (Walters Davies & Davis 1973). The majority of pairs attempt to breed annually once they have bred for the first time. However, there are a small number of cases in Wales where established pairs have apparently missed a year of breeding before resuming again in the following year (Davis et al. 2001). This may be the result of poor weather or a lack of food which makes it harder for paired birds to get into breeding condition.

The early season

Unlike many birds of prey, including the Buzzard with which it so often shares the same countryside, the Red Kite does not defend exclusive feeding territories from others of its own kind. It does, however, defend a small area around the nest site, usually extending to no more than a few hundred metres from the nest itself. A radius of 80m from the nest, or an area of 1-3 hectares was suggested by Bustamante and Hiraldo (1993). First-year birds passing near to the nest area are sometimes ignored, probably because Red Kites do not normally breed until they are at least two years old and so the established breeding pair may not consider these youngsters to be a significant threat. Intruding adults, on the other hand, are more likely to be on the lookout for a breeding site or even a mate and are often chased away vigorously. Mougeot (2000) found that the resident male would attack a decoy bird, painted to look like an adult, and placed close to the nest of an established pair early in the season.

Courtship display lacks the flamboyance seen in some other birds of prey and is mainly restricted to slow circling above the nest wood involving one or both members of the pair. From just above the level of the trees, a pair may ascend to a considerable height, becoming mere specks in the sky or even disappearing into low clouds, before descending again. Sometimes a period of circling ends with a bird folding back its wings and plunging down though the canopy into the wood, usually close to the nest tree or the location where the nest will subsequently be built.

Another form of display commonly seen near the breeding site involves two birds flying very close together with one following closely behind the other and both using deep, exaggerated wing-beats. It is sometimes followed by a vigorous pursuit, as if one bird is trying to drive away the other, but is believed to mainly involve display between members of an established breeding pair (Hardy et al. 2006). This display is also seen well away from the nearest breeding site, and even outside the breeding season, when it possibly involves birds trying to assess each other as potential mates. A similar type of 'butterfly' display-flight is performed by unpaired birds holding territory, sometimes at considerable height, when it may serve as a means of attracting a potential mate. Red Kites become more vocal in the breeding season and their shrill, whinnying calls, made either in flight or from a perch, are a familiar sound in areas where the bird is common.

More spectacular aerial activity, including talon-grappling and rapid, roller-coaster chases, sometimes takes place between members of a pair but also occurs during aggressive encounters between rival birds. In one extreme incident, wit-nessed by Peter Davis in Wales, two birds with talons interlocked spiralled downwards together and ended up crashing into the woodland canopy. Sim-ilar incidents involving birds with interlocked talons have been witnessed in

DAN POWELL

Yorkshire and Sussex in recent years (e.g. Kalaher 2005). Rather more unfortunate were 'two males' described by Montagu (1833):

> [They were] so intent in combat, that they both fell to the ground, holding firmly by each other's talons, and actually suffered themselves to be killed by a woodman who was close by, and who demolished them both with his bill-hook.

Limited territorial activity can be seen throughout the year but it becomes far more frequent and noticeable in early spring. In Britain, birds are most active in March in the weeks leading up to nest building and egg laying, making this the best month for fieldworkers to try to locate breeding pairs (Wotton *et al*. 2002, Hardy *et al*. 2006).

It is not unusual for a pair of Red Kites that are apparently settled on a territory early in the season, to suddenly switch to an alternative site, up to several kilometres away, in some cases even after a nest has been built or refurbished. This may be the result of disturbance at the initial site but some pairs are perhaps simply undecided as to which breeding site to use until just before the eggs are laid. Several important factors, such as the degree of human disturbance or the number of potential nest predators in an area, can only be assessed reliably by spending time on a territory and it seems that some pairs spend time at two or more sites before committing themselves to the most suitable. This behaviour is frustrating for fieldworkers as Red Kites are at their most active in their territories early in the season. Breeding pairs may be located relatively easily at this stage, only, in some cases, to be absent when the site is visited again later in the season.

The nest site

Although the Red Kite is not at all fussy about the species of tree used for nesting, there is a preference for trees large enough to provide a suitable secure fork in which to lodge the nest. In Wales, nests have been found at heights of 4-30m with the majority being between about 12 and 15m (Cross & Davis 1998). In southern England, the majority of nests are over 15m high, mainly because the beech trees so often used have few substantial branches below this height. Snell *et al*. (2002) found 72 nests in beech trees in the Chilterns in 2000 with the next most popular choices of oak and larch each being used by just four pairs. In central and northern Spain, nest height varies considerably depending on the species of tree used. Those in poplars are often well above 15m, whereas nests in the smaller pines tend to be much lower. In Germany, there is also considerable variation with nests found in the range 4-30m and an average height of approximately 18-20m (Ortlieb 1989).

The Red Kite, with its large wing-span, requires a good aerial route to the nest and therefore generally chooses an open site with well-spaced trees, often close to the edge of a wood, or adjacent to a woodland ride or clearing. For this reason, unthinned commercial plantations, where the trees are densely packed together with few large gaps, are mostly avoided. The frequent use of oak woods in mid-Wales (Newton *et al.* 1981) and beech woods in southern England reflects the abundance of these two woodland types in the respective areas. In central England there is a greater mix of different species and, despite an apparent overall preference for oaks, a wide variety of different tree species have already been used (Table 11). In northern Scotland, a wide variety of tree species are also used, with Scots pine the most frequently recorded, reflecting its abundance in the area (Brian Etheridge pers. comm.).

Red Kites usually choose a substantial fork in a mature tree for their nest site, building the nest either against the main trunk or among branches within the canopy. A particularly favoured location is the point where the main trunk splits into smaller branches that spread upwards into the canopy as this provides a secure fork with many supporting branches against which to lodge the nest structure. Less often, the nest is built resting precariously on a branch some distance out from the main trunk where there is a risk of collapse in high

Table 11: **Red Kite nest sites in central England, 1996-2000**

Tree species	No. nests	Nest height Average (range) in metres
Broadleaf		
Oak (English/Sessile)	18	15 (11-20)
Turkey Oak	1	20
Field Maple	1	10
Sycamore	1	15
Ash	2	18
Conifer		
Norway Spruce	3	10 (8-12)
Scots Pine	3	14 (9-17)
Larch	2	15.5 (11-20)
Total	**31**	**15 (8-20)**

winds. One nest in central England, built by an inexperienced first-year pair, was constructed on the flimsiest of horizontal branches about 10m high in a small spruce tree, despite an abundance of large mature oaks nearby. Each time the incubating bird left the nest, the branch shook alarmingly and this was the probable cause of subsequent breeding failure. An intact egg found on the ground below the abandoned nest had almost certainly been accidentally ejected due to the unstable position of the nest.

Although the great majority of nests are in trees, Red Kites have been recorded building nests on cliff-ledges or crags in Majorca, Spain and Sicily (Javier Viñuela pers. comm.). This has also been recorded on the Cape Verde Islands where it may have involved hybrids between Red and Black Kites. Pylons are used occasionally in central Europe (Hagemeijer & Blair 1997). Very occasionally, nests are constructed on the ground, as occurred in Northumbria in 2005, involving inexperienced first-year birds. Not surprisingly no eggs were laid and the pair quickly lost interest.

The majority of nest building is concentrated into a few weeks (sometimes even a few days) with most activity in Britain in March and early April, just before the eggs are laid. The odd stick may be added to a nest at almost any time from January onwards and new material is brought in sporadically throughout the breeding season. A pair in Wales even built a fairly substantial nest in late September and early October but quickly lost interest as the weather turned colder (Cross & Davis 2005). Both the male and female are involved in nest construction, using sticks collected from the ground or broken from growing trees, and nest-building activity is often concentrated into the early and latter parts of the day. Observations at breeding sites suggest that it is the male that brings in the majority of the nest material whilst the female does most of the actual nest building.

Unpaired birds, including first-years with no real intention of breeding, are often seen carrying nest material. This may be repeatedly dropped and re-caught in what seems to be no more than a game. As with other forms of play (see Chapter 9), this behaviour is probably best interpreted as practice for the time when the bird is paired up and needs to build a nest for the first time.

The nest is similar in form to that of a Carrion Crow but generally larger and more untidy, with large sticks placed in a seemingly rather haphazard manner to form a platform about two feet across. The rather shallow cup, which soon becomes almost completely flat, is lined with soft, dry material such as dry grass, fur, or sheep's wool to provide a secure pad for the eggs. In Britain wool is the favoured material and is found in the lining of virtually every nest when it is available in the local countryside. A Red Kite seen flying towards a nest site with wool in its beak or trailing from its feet in early April is a good sign that the clutch will soon be laid.

Established Red Kite pairs sometimes build a new nest, often using an old Grey Squirrel drey, or a Carrion Crow or Buzzard nest as a base, rather than starting from scratch. In northern Scotland an old Osprey nest has been used on at least one occasion. They may instead refurbish one of their own nests used in a previous year, with long-established pairs having as many as five alternatives from which to choose. Nests that are used repeatedly, with new material added each year, can become massive structures and early in the season before the surrounding trees have leaves, they are very obvious from some distance away. Other species sometimes make use of active Red Kite nests to rear their own young. Sparrows are well-known for nesting within White Stork nests and Tree Sparrows also use the nests of both Black and Red Kites in Spain and perhaps elsewhere. In northern Scotland, House Sparrows have been recorded nesting within a Red Kite nest (Brian Etheridge pers. comm.). It is likely that these birds benefit not only from the secure structure provided by the nest, but also the protection from nest predators that results from the presence of the adult Red Kites.

Walters Davies and Davis (1973) found that Welsh pairs were more likely to use an alternative nest following a breeding failure in the previous year. In a study of 133 pairs, 40% of the 68 nests where the pair had failed were used in the following year, whereas the figure was 80% for the 65 nests where at least one chick fledged. This study excluded territories apparently containing only one nest where the birds had no choice of an alternative other than building a new nest from scratch. The same pattern is apparent in northern Scotland, where between 1992 and 2000, 65% of 85 successful pairs reused the same nest the following year, but only 11% of 18 failed pairs did so (Brian Etheridge pers. comm.). In southern England, 56% of successful pairs, whose composition did not change between years, reused the same nest the following year (Evans *et al.* 1999), whereas in central England, only one of 15 pairs that bred in successive years reused the same nest. It may be that the tendency to reuse nests is more frequent in well established populations with a higher proportion of more experienced breeding pairs.

One theory put forward to explain why birds of prey have alternative nest-sites is that such behaviour is a means of avoiding parasites (Newton 1979). These may remain in a nest from one season to the next, ready to infest birds when they return in the following year. The behaviour of the Red Kite in Britain suggests that this is not the primary reason for building new nests. Nests where chicks are reared successfully, and are therefore in the nest for a long period of time, are likely to support the highest parasite burdens, yet it is these nests that are most frequently used again.

Nest decoration

Some birds of prey, including the Buzzard, place twigs with fresh green leaves in the nest before the eggs are laid. Red Kites also 'decorate' their nests but, rather than greenery, they prefer to use rubbish, including paper, rags and scraps of plastic. This material can often be seen hanging down from the side of an active nest or found on the ground below. It is possible that some of these items are intended to form part of the nest lining but become dislodged and end up caught on sticks at the edge of the nest. It is likely, however, that the majority is used purposefully as a form of decoration, perhaps serving to advertise to other Red Kites in the area that the nest is in use. Material brought in by the male may also help to demonstrate his nest-building prowess to the female and so help strengthen the pair-bond. It is certainly not a new habit and in Shakespeare's *The Winter's Tale* the character Autolicus referred to it when he warned 'When the Kite builds, look to lesser linen.' In those days, washing was left to dry on the top of hedges and the Red Kite was clearly not slow to take advantage. It also had a reputation for stealing headwear, apparently sometimes snatched from the wearer, and this led to it being known as the 'hat bird' in some places.

Lord Lilford, on a visit to central Spain in 1865, was told by a local that a purse containing nine dollars had once been found in a Red Kite's nest. And on the same trip, Lilford himself apparently learnt of the death of President Lincoln from a scrap of Spanish newspaper found at a nest near Aranjuez (Lilford 1883). Other odd examples of nest material have been unearthed by Cocker and Mabey (2005), perhaps the most surprising being the supposed habit of 'plucking hair off men's heads to weave into the nest' originally recorded by the Roman author Aelian.

The reintroduced birds in Britain are able to take advantage of a range of modern items including crisp packets and supermarket bags, as well as the handkerchiefs, socks and underwear which were no doubt a mainstay of nest-decoration centuries ago and to which Shakespeare's warning referred. Other oddities found at nests in recent years, have included a lottery ticket (unsuccessful), a plastic model dog, a tennis ball and even the polystyrene-encased data-gathering box from a weather balloon! The two halves of a teddy-bear were found at a nest in southern England, whilst the head of another was discovered at a nest in Yorkshire in 2000.

Orientation of nest sites

It is well known that some birds of prey tend to select nest sites facing in a particular direction more often than would be expected by chance. Watson (1997) found that Golden Eagles in Scotland preferred sites facing to the north or east rather than to the south or west, and suggested that this was either to avoid exposure to inclement weather, which comes mainly from the southwest, or to avoid excessive exposure to the sun, thereby reducing the risk of the chicks over-heating. Evidence from studies of Golden Eagles elsewhere in Europe suggests that the latter is the more likely explanation (Jordano 1981, Tjernberg 1983). Viñuela and Sunyer (1992) showed that Black Kites in central and southern Spain favoured the east or southeast side of the crown of a tree in which to build their nests. In southern Spain, hatching success was lower for nests located in non-preferred directions and it was thought most likely that this resulted from increased exposure to prevailing winds and rainfall, which could cause nests to flood.

Newton *et al.* (1981) included orientation among the factors they considered when studying the locations of Red Kite nests in Wales between 1946 and 1978. A considerably higher number of nests were in woods on slopes facing to the north or east than to the south or west. The favoured direction was northeast with 29% of nests facing in this direction. In contrast, significantly fewer nests were on slopes facing south (8%), southwest (8%) and west (4%). Whatever the reasons for this preference, the authors found no difference in breeding productivity between nests facing in different directions in Wales. If, as is likely with the Golden Eagle, a tendency to avoid sites facing to the south and west evolved in order to reduce the risk of the chicks overheating, then the cool Welsh climate may nullify any possible disadvantage when such sites are used. Those involved in monitoring the reintroduced birds in southern England have also recorded a preference for nesting at the north-eastern edges of woods (Snell et al. 2002) and it would be interesting to know if this resulted in any advantage in terms of breeding success in this area.

Dee Doody, who studied Red Kites in Wales for many years, believes that there is another reason why woods on slopes facing northeast are preferred. He argues that access to a nest site is made easier if the adults are able to approach from downwind and, with a prevailing south-westerly wind, this is most often possible at sites sloping to the northeast. It is certainly true that when flying to perch in a tree, Red Kites approaching from upwind often fly directly over the tree, turn, and head back into the wind before coming to rest. It is clearly easier for them to fly at a slow enough speed to judge the landing properly when they are flying into the wind. Nevertheless, this is likely to be of only secondary importance when it comes to selecting a nest site.

Egg laying, incubation and the early chick stage

As the time for laying approaches, the female spends increasing amounts of time close to the nest and becomes much less active, relying more and more on the male to provision her with food. The adult birds are far less obvious around the nest site than earlier in the season, with the female spending most time either on the nest or perching quietly close by, and the male doing the same when not away from the area searching for food. At this stage, searching likely woodland for the large nest structure is one of the most effective methods for locating breeding pairs, although this becomes more difficult once the trees have come into leaf.

Copulations become frequent in the days before the first egg is laid, often occurring soon after the male has brought food to a perch within the nest wood. Mougeot (2000) studied 16 Red Kite pairs in Corsica and found that there were, on average, 234 copulations for each clutch, beginning up to 40 days before the first egg was laid. Early matings, well before the female becomes fertile, may play a role in pair-bonding and mate assessment. By mating so frequently, the male is also attempting to make sure that it is his sperm that fertilises the eggs and not that of a rival male who may have mated with the female whilst he was away searching for food. The alternative strategy of 'mate-guarding' is used by male birds of some species but is not always possible in birds of prey because the male is responsible for finding food for both himself and the female at this stage of the breeding cycle. He is therefore forced to spend time foraging away from the nest site where the female spends most of her time. Despite this, male Red Kites do not abandon the mate-guarding strategy altogether. Mougeot (2000) found that males at nest sites where other pairs were nesting nearby spent more time close to the nest during the pre-laying period than did males from more isolated pairs. This suggests that they are well aware of the threat from rival males and keep foraging flights away from the nest to a minimum.

Extra-pair copulation, where a rival male mates with a paired female, is known to occur in Red Kites, although it has only been recorded infrequently (Mougeot 2000). In Wales, Davis et al. (2001) recorded a male bird repeatedly visiting the nests of two other pairs, both about 2km away from his own nest, while his female was on eggs. Although no extra-pair mating was witnessed, it seems likely that this bird was on the lookout for such an opportunity. This behaviour provides a possible explanation for the fact that inexperienced, first-time breeders in the reintroduced populations in Britain sometimes select relatively isolated nest sites, well away from other breeding birds. Due to inexperience, the male from such pairs is likely to have to spend long periods away from the nest in order to locate sufficient food for himself and the female in the period before egg-laying. With the female unattended for long periods, unwelcome intrusions from other males are a serious concern. The risks are reduced, however, if there are few other breeding birds in the area.

In Britain, most pairs lay 2-3 eggs with clutches of one and four relatively uncommon. Table 12 shows the relative frequency with which different clutches are laid in central Wales. Two eggs are far more common than three eggs, whereas in more suitable lowland habitat in England, Scotland and continental Europe, three-egg clutches are most common (Ortlieb 1989, Evans et al. 1999). Occasional clutches of five eggs have been recorded in central Europe (Glutz von Blotzheim et al. 1971, Hille 1995a). Most pairs in Britain lay during the first three weeks in April with the Welsh and English birds laying, on average, slightly earlier than the Scottish birds. There is a certain amount of variation, even amongst birds breeding in the same area, with some pairs already incubating by late March and others not laying until late April or even early-mid May. Laying dates in central Europe are similar. A long-term study of Red Kites breeding in the Hakel Forest in eastern Germany found that the start of incubation varied

Table 12: **Clutch size in Welsh Red Kite nests, 1946-1996** *(from Cross & Davis 2005)*

No. Eggs	No. Clutches	Percentage
1	51	6.8
2	399	53.5
3	281	37.7
4	15	2.0

Mean clutch size: 2.3 (n=746)

from 20 March to 16 May, with a median date of 13 April. Of 858 clutches observed between 1958 and 1993, over 85% were laid sometime during the first three weeks in April (Mammen & Stubbe 1995). In southern Europe, birds in Spain, southern Italy and Corsica begin laying as early as late February or early March, well in advance of populations further north, although laying continues into April and May (Gaibani *et al*. 2001, Mougeot & Bretagnolle 2006). The Hakel Forest study showed that the earlier laid clutches tended to produce more young than those laid later and overall breeding success was higher in the years when the majority of clutches were laid earlier than usual. Dixon (2001) found that the same was true for breeding birds in southern England. This conforms to a general pattern found in many bird species and results from the fact that the fittest individuals are generally able to attain breeding condition earlier in the season (Newton 1979).

Only a single clutch is laid unless the eggs are lost early during the incubation period. If this happens then the pair may lay a replacement clutch, often in a new nest within the same territory. Late clutches in Britain, laid during late April or early May, involve a combination of re-lays, following an earlier nest failure, and inexperienced first-time breeders that usually lay later than more experienced breeding pairs. Glutz von Blotzheim *et al*. (1971) found that for 109 breeding attempts in Germany, the mean brood size was 2.14 for first clutches and only 1.65 for replacements, the lower productivity for re-laid clutches reflecting the extra resources used up by the adult birds in producing the second clutch.

The female carries out the majority of incubation, either relying on food brought in by the male, or leaving the nest for short periods in order to feed, while the male takes over the nest duties. At one nest in central England, involving a pair of first-year birds, it was possible to check the sex of the incubating bird regularly by radio-tracking. On only three out of 21 checks was the male found to be on the nest. At several different breeding sites in the same area, where the adults could be identified from wing-tags, males were seen sitting on the nest on only six out of 38 visits (Carter & Grice 2002). During poor weather, the female may not risk leaving the eggs for even a short period of time. At one

Red Kite eggs are, on average, slightly larger than a typical chicken's egg at approximately 57 × 45mm. They are usually laid on a pad of wool as at this nest in central Wales (Tony Cross)

These unhatched eggs from nests in England show the variation in shape and a typical range of markings (Ian Carter)

Welsh nest monitored using a nest camera, the female remained almost motionless for a period of 36 hours during wet and windy conditions (Cross & Davis 1998), and at a nest in northern Scotland, a late, overnight, fall of snow in April covered a nest including the wings and tail of the incubating female. When Brian Etheridge visited the nest site at dawn to check on the pair, only the bird's head, with its gleaming yellow eye, was visible above the blanket of white. Researchers in Wales used a light-sensitive false egg that was placed in nests in order to show for how long each day the eggs were left uncovered. Each time the egg was exposed to light, a radio-transmitter within it pulsed at a higher rate, showing that it was no longer being incubated. This work confirmed that the adults were extremely attentive and the eggs were left uncovered for only a few minutes each day (Lovegrove *et al*. 1990).

Red Kite eggs hatch after around 31-32 days of incubation (Snow & Perrins 1998). The incubation period has been quoted in various sources from 28 days to as much as 37-38 days. The differences stem from a combination of natural variation, the inaccuracy of measurements, and confusion as to how the incubation period is defined. Some authors have referred to the time taken for a single egg to hatch whilst others have given the time for the whole clutch. The female may cover the first laid eggs, in order to protect them, without actually incubating, and this period has been included in some estimates for the length of incubation. It is also the case that a female may adopt a position on a nest as if she is covering or incubating eggs when, in fact, they have yet to be laid. If the eggs do not hatch, as a result of infertility, or because the chicks within have failed to develop properly, the female may continue sitting for up to several weeks beyond the normal incubation period before finally giving up.

Once the eggs have hatched, the small chicks are brooded by the female for most of the first 2-3 weeks while they are still covered with down and vulnerable to cool, damp, conditions, as well as predators. Chicks older than this may be covered in poor weather and at night, although, with a brood of three or four, this quickly becomes an impossibly difficult task. It is the male that provides the majority of the food for the chicks, particularly during the first few weeks when the female spends almost all of her time, on, or close to, the nest.

In many birds of prey and owls, eggs are laid at regular intervals and incubation begins before the final egg is laid so that the eggs hatch at intervals and there is a subsequent size difference between the chicks. This is known as the 'brood reduction strategy' and it has evolved to allow birds to cope with an unpredictable food supply (Newton 1979). If there is abundant food then all the chicks get an adequate supply and all survive to fledging age. If there is a shortage then the largest chicks grab more than their fair share leaving their smaller siblings to starve. In some species, the older chick will attack its younger siblings when food is short, sometimes killing and eating them. Brutal though this sounds, it does help to ensure that when conditions are poor, at least some of the brood survive. If an inadequate food supply were to be shared equally then there might not be sufficient for any of the chicks to develop properly.

There has been some uncertainty regarding the extent to which the Red Kite adopts this strategy. Whilst it is well known that there is an interval of 1-3 days between the laying of each egg, the time when incubation actually begins is not always easy to determine. In the late 1980s, the RSPB carried out some research in mid-Wales which involved the installation of video cameras at nest sites (Lovegrove et al. 1990). The pictures showed that the eggs usually hatched at three-day intervals, so, in this case, incubation must have started as soon as

Figure 6: **Feeding bouts (graphs) and number of attacks (histograms) for two Welsh nestlings monitored by video camera** *(from Lovegrove* et al. *1990)*

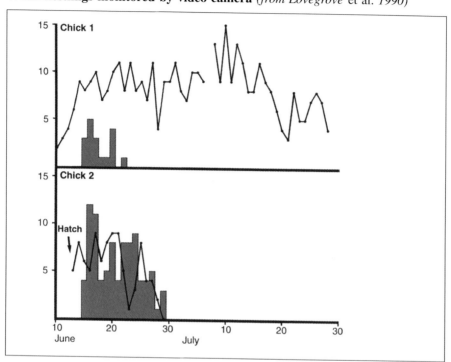

the first egg was laid. At two of the five nests monitored in this way, video pictures showed the largest chick in the nest repeatedly attacking its smaller sibling. In each case, both chicks in the nests initially grew well but, after about five days, the larger chick became aggressive each time food was brought to the nest. The smaller chick fought back at first but became progressively weaker until it eventually died (Figure 6).

Researchers in southern Spain found a similar pattern of brood reduction, with 19 out of a sample of 37 nests losing at least one chick (attributed to starvation) before fledging (Veiga & Hiraldo 1990). This study also determined the period taken for all the eggs in a clutch to hatch and, surprisingly, found considerable variation. Most eggs from a sample of 12 two-egg clutches hatched within a single day of each other and only one had the three day interval found in Wales. The hatching interval for three-egg clutches varied from one day to as much as 12 days (for the whole clutch to hatch) with most of the sample of nine nests somewhere in between. Clutches with the longest hatching period, and therefore the largest size difference between chicks, were more likely to suffer brood reduction due to the loss of the smallest chick. Ortlieb (1989) reported similar variation in Germany, although a gap of 2-3 days between the hatching of each egg was thought to be typical.

Live pictures from cameras installed at nests in England and Scotland have repeatedly shown that the smallest chick in the brood is attacked by its larger siblings during the first few weeks in the nest. But, in contrast to the situation in Wales, the weakest chick is usually able to withstand these attacks provided that the adults continue to bring in enough food to meet the requirements of the whole brood. The attacks quickly diminish as the chicks develop and the nest becomes an altogether more harmonious place once the chicks reach about 3-4 weeks.

In summary, studies across the Red Kite's range clearly show that incubation does not always begin with the first laid egg and, in some cases, starts just before the final egg is laid. It is possible that, as has been found in the Common Kestrel (Wiebe *et al*. 1998), the adult birds are able to manipulate hatching patterns through variations in incubation behaviour, in response to food availability and the degree to which the food supply is predictable. Further study is required to find out if this is indeed the case in Red Kites.

The growing brood

When the chicks are small they are fed on manageable pieces of meat by one of the adults, as, at this stage, they are unable to tear carcasses apart for themselves. As is the case with many birds of prey, this task is mainly performed by the female, although male Red Kites have also been recorded feeding young. At a nest site in northern Scotland, footage from a camera set up to provide live pictures to a nearby visitor centre, revealed that the male bird was particularly attentive and regularly fed the chicks, at times even in the presence of the female. Males have also been observed on camera feeding the young at nests in central and southern England.

A detailed study of a nest in central England with only a single chick, showed that the male brought in almost all of the food required and the female remained close to the nest for the majority of the brood-rearing period (Medina 2000). She was therefore on hand to protect the chick from potential predators and to cover it during spells of wet weather. At nests where there are more chicks to rear, or where prey is not so abundant, the male may not be able to find all the food that is required on his own and the female must then spend more time foraging away from the nest. In this situation there is a trade off between food provisioning and protection of the chicks. If both adults are away from the nest, there is a greater risk to the chicks, but, unless sufficient food is brought in, they are unlikely to survive in any case. As the chicks grow larger they require more food but become less vulnerable to predation and so the female is more likely to leave the nest for longer periods. In exceptional circumstances, a female is capable of rearing young without any help from the male, undertaking all of the nest defence and food provisioning duties. This was recorded by Van Kleef and Bustamante (1999) in southern Spain, where a male was paired to two females but helped only one to rear young. The lone female managed to successfully rear a single chick to fledging. In northern Scotland, a female successfully reared a single chick when the male bird was killed soon after the eggs had hatched (Brian Etheridge pers. comm.).

The growth rate of the chicks varies to some extent, depending on the amount of food provided by the adults. When food is in short supply, the growth rate drops so that most of the available resources can be channelled into self-maintenance (Viñuela & Ferrer 1997). This is an important adaptation for situations where the food supply is unpredictable, as it allows the young to survive a period of food shortage before resuming more rapid growth when food becomes easier to find. The initial size difference between chicks in a nest may become exaggerated when food is short, as the largest individual is likely to grab the majority and continue to grow rapidly, whilst the smallest receives barely enough to remain alive. Although the age of nestlings can be estimated, by taking measurements of tarsus length or wing length, for example, and comparing these with measurements taken from birds of known age (Hardy et al. 2006), the variation in growth rates between individuals means that this method is subject to considerable inaccuracy.

After 3-4 weeks the chicks begin to feed themselves from food items left on the nest, although the adults continue to offer assistance at times for several more weeks. The amount of food items delivered to the nest each day varies considerably depending on the foraging success of the adult birds and the size of the prey brought in. Based on limited observations at nests in central England, 5-10 food deliveries per day would appear to be typical, with more activity in the morning than after midday. If the adult birds are able to bring in a surplus of food, the nest platform can become, at least from a human point of view, a decidedly unpleasant place, with swarms of flies in constant attendance and maggots crawling over the uneaten meat. The maggots are no doubt often consumed along with the partly decomposed carcasses and the flies at least offer a target for the chicks to snap at in their more playful moments!

Despite such apparently unhygienic conditions, the chicks do at least endeavour to keep the nest free from droppings. From a very early age they perform an ungainly and somewhat comical manoeuvre that involves backing to the edge of the nest and squirting their liquid faeces out over the side. After the chicks have been in the nest for some time, the ground below becomes spattered with 'white-wash'. The chicks squirt the droppings over a greater distance as they develop and, as with other birds of prey, experienced observers are able to use the amount of white-wash and the maximum distance it appears away from the nest to estimate the number and approximate age of the chicks present. Although this behaviour results in a cleaner nest and probably reduces the threat of disease, it is not without its risks. A nest camera in northern Scotland caught the moment when one of the three chicks backed to the edge of the nest to perform its usual duty. As it got close to the edge it suddenly lost its balance and, despite valiant attempts to hold on, eventually fell to the ground below, leaving the remaining chicks on the nest looking somewhat bemused. Remarkably, the chick was not injured in the fall and fieldworkers, having been alerted by the live pictures, were able to return it to the nest where it subsequently fledged successfully.

Fledging to independence

At about 5-6 weeks the chicks begin to spend much of their time standing on the nest platform, regularly spreading and flapping their wings in order to strengthen their flight muscles. There is then a gradual progression towards the first flight, which normally occurs after about 7-8 weeks in the nest. Bustamante (1993), working in southern Spain, found that the time taken to fledging for a sample of 37 chicks varied from 47 to 78 days, with an average of 55 days (almost eight weeks). Such wide variation results mainly from differences in the growth rates of the nestlings which is, in turn, dependent on the amount of food provided by the adults.

As the young approach fledging age they become increasingly active and adventurous, often clambering onto branches adjacent to the nest by the time they are about six weeks old. Some birds attempt their first flight before they are able to fly strongly and, in so doing, take a considerable risk. Chicks close to fledging age are regularly found on the ground near to the nest-tree having presumably lost height and crash-landed when trying to fly from the nest. Here, they are unlikely to be fed by the adult birds and they are also vulnerable to ground predators. Unless they can clamber up onto a perch, or are found by fieldworkers during a routine nest visit and can be replaced on the nest or a high perch, they are unlikely to survive.

Well-grown nestlings and recently fledged young have a distinctive call, quite unlike both the thin, high-pitched piping calls of small nestlings and the typical calls of full-grown birds. It is higher in pitch than the adult calls, with an upward inflection that makes it superficially similar to the call of a Curlew. It can be given singly but is often rapidly repeated, sometimes rising to an excited crescendo with the arrival of an adult carrying food.

Recently fledged birds remain dependent on their parents for several weeks, during which time they remain close to the nest while the adults continue to bring food, either to the nest or a nearby feeding perch. Often both adults are involved in the food provisioning of fledged young but, especially where food is plentiful, this task appears to be carried out mainly by the male and the female may spend long periods away from the nest area with little further involvement in rearing the young. This pattern of behaviour was observed at three nest sites in central England in 1999 and 2000, in two cases involving a first-year female and an adult male. It has also been regularly reported in other birds of prey including Montagu's Harrier (Clarke 1996) and Black-shouldered Kite (Newton 1979).

The amount of food brought to the nest by the adults tends to decrease gradually after the young have fledged, and young are forced to start finding food for themselves when the supply has dried up completely. Bustamante (1993) suggested that young Red Kites in southern Spain did not start to forage for themselves until they were forced to do so, as live-capture traps, baited with meat and placed close to the nest site, failed to interest juveniles whilst the adults were still bringing in food. Studies of chicks fitted with radio-transmitters in England have shown that fledglings reach independence on average about 3-4 weeks after their first flight, although there is some variation (Dixon 2001, pers. obs.). Workers in southern Spain found that the post-fledging dependence period varied from as little as 11 days to a maximum of 40 days, with an average of 26 days, similar to the period found in England (Bustamante 1993). These figures, based on intensive studies, are considerably shorter than the previous general estimate of 28-70 days given by Newton (1979). During the dependence period, the young become increasingly adventurous, progressing from short, flapping flights between trees close to the nest in the first few days, to soaring high above the nest wood after 2-3 weeks.

Young birds that are no longer being provisioned by their parents sometimes try to take advantage of other breeding pairs in the same area that are still bringing food to the nest. A camera at a nest in central England revealed that a tagged juvenile from a nest 2km away made visits on 17 days during a 25 day period and took advantage of at least 15 food-drops from both the male and female of the resident pair (Agombar 2003). At the same site, another juvenile from a nest 8km away, about four weeks older than the resident fledglings, also visited the nest regularly. The adults continued to bring in food for over six

weeks after their own young had fledged and for the final two weeks, when their young had become independent, were feeding only the unrelated young. Similar behaviour has also been recorded in Wales (Davis *et al.* 2001) and in Spain (Bustamante & Hiraldo 1990, 1993). It would appear that the adult birds are unable to distinguish between their own young and unrelated young and respond instinctively to the presence of young on the nest by providing food. Interestingly, such 'adoptions' are more common in Spain in Red Kites than in the closely related Black Kite. Adult Black Kites, unlike Red Kites, appear able to recognise intruding, unrelated juveniles and regularly chase them away from the nest. The most likely explanation is that in the semi-colonial Black Kite, where nests are often very close together, the risk of investing time and effort in feeding unrelated juveniles is high and so this species has evolved an ability to recognise intruders. The risk of intruders appearing at nests is much reduced in the Red Kite, as nests are usually more widely spaced, and so the ability to recognise unrelated juveniles has not evolved (Bustamante & Hiraldo 1990, 1993).

Contrary to some early accounts, there is no evidence to suggest that young Red Kites follow adults on foraging trips or that a bond with either parents or siblings is maintained once the association with the nest and its immediate vicinity has been lost. The mainly scavenging lifestyle of the Red Kite requires no specialised hunting techniques and so, unlike in some birds of prey, the adult birds do not need to play an active role in teaching young birds how to obtain food. Red Kites are social birds and adults are sometimes seen in the same area as their young (individually identifiable by wing-tags or radio-tracking), well away from the nest site. But this appears to be no more than a chance occurrence and juveniles and adults are also regularly seen in close association with unrelated birds. It is perhaps the fact that small, mixed groups of adult and young Red Kites are often encountered in autumn and winter that led some to assume in the past that these were family groups.

Nest predators

The Red Kite's relationship with corvids, particularly Ravens in Wales and Carrion or Hooded Crows throughout Britain, alters radically during the breeding season. These opportunist species are potential predators of eggs and small chicks and, even before the eggs are laid, individuals flying too close to the nest site are attacked and chased with a vigour that seems strangely out of character for a bird that normally adopts a far more leisurely flight. The attacks rarely result in physical contact but an intruding corvid is sometimes pursued for several hundred metres before the Red Kite gives up and heads back to the nest area. From a human standpoint, it is tempting to believe that such aggression is fuelled by a desire for revenge as, for most of the year, it is the Red Kite on the receiving end of interactions between the two species (see Chapter 9). In reality, the attacks serve a very useful purpose in persuading the corvids to move away from the area so that they are not able to threaten the eggs or nestlings. As a result of antagonism between Red Kites and Carrion Crows it is unusual to find active nests of the two species within about 200m or so of each other. This is not always the case, however, and the two species have even been found nesting in the same individual tree on one occasion in central Wales (Tony Cross pers. comm.).

In Wales, Ravens and Red Kites have a particularly uneasy relationship in the breeding season and a Red Kite pair nesting close to an active Raven nest will often fail to fledge any young (Davis & Newton 1981). The main problem comes when the Raven young fledge, which often occurs whilst the Red Kite chicks are still small. If the young Ravens stray too close to the Red Kite nest then the adults of both species become involved, each fearing for the safety of their own young. In one extreme case, investigated by Tony Cross, an adult Red Kite was killed following direct aggression from one of the adult Ravens. When the Welsh population was still small and vulnerable, preventative measures were taken to avoid conflict between Red Kites and the far more numerous Raven. This involved removing eggs from Raven nests, under licence, if a Red Kite pair was nesting nearby, and placing them in alternative Raven nests to be reared by surrogate parents well out of harms way. On the other side of the Atlantic, Ravens have caused even greater problems by predating the eggs of the rare and threatened California Condor. In order to protect such a highly endangered species, conservationists have resorted to shooting Ravens nesting in the same area (Snyder & Snyder 2000).

Other birds of prey are sometimes chased aggressively by adult Red Kites if they stray too close to an active nest. In Britain, Buzzards are a frequent source of irritation if a pair is holding territory in the same wood, and there may be frequent bouts of aerial sparring. The two species are relatively evenly matched during these aerial battles with the threat carried by the Buzzard's superior power counteracted by the greater manoeuvrability of the Red Kite. Perhaps, for this reason, most interactions end with neither species gaining the upper hand. Buzzards and Red Kites no doubt sometimes displace each other from territories but in some situations they learn to tolerate each other and it is not uncommon to find them nesting in close proximity in the same area of woodland. However, more serious disputes do take place on occasion. One dispute, at a nest site in Sussex, ended with an adult Red Kite grabbing at the breast of a Buzzard causing it to lose a large number of feathers (Kalaher 2005). In an incident in northern Scotland, where the two species were nesting about 100m apart, a recently fledged juvenile Red Kite was found decapitated below the Buzzard nest, having almost certainly been predated by one of the adult Buzzards. In another incident in the same area where the two species were again nesting close together, Buzzards were suspected of attacking four-week-old Red Kite chicks in their nest. One chick was found dead below its nest with another emaciated live chick found nearby (Brian Etheridge pers. comm.).

In Doñana National Park in southern Spain, adult Red Kites aggressively chase Black Kites, Booted Eagles and Imperial Eagles, as well as individuals of their own kind that fly too close to nests with chicks or recently fledged young (Bustamante & Hiraldo 1993). A study based on prolonged observations at nest sites found that levels of aggression tended to decline during the weeks following fledging, probably because, as the young mature, they become less vulnerable to predators. The study also found that Imperial Eagles were chased more vigorously than the other species suggesting that the adult Red Kites viewed them as the greatest threat to their young. A leg-ring from a recently fledged Red Kite was found under a perch habitually used by an Imperial Eagle, suggesting that the threat from this species was very real (González 1989). The Goshawk is another bird of prey that takes the young of other raptors (Kenward 2006) and could pose a potential threat to nestling Red Kites. In Germany, researchers have used a stuffed Eagle Owl as a decoy in order to trap adult Red Kites close to their nest site. This technique takes advantage of the fact that the Eagle Owl is seen as a threat by the Red Kites and is often attacked, allowing the attacking bird to be caught in a suitably placed trap.

The activities of mammalian predators are harder to observe due to their unobtrusive behaviour. In Britain, the introduced Grey Squirrel is certainly a potential predator of unguarded small chicks and eggs. In Scotland, Pine Martens have been suspected of taking eggs or small young on a number of occasions. In southern Spain, Sergio *et al*. (2005) found that one of the main causes of breeding failure was nest predation by mammals, most likely Iberian Lynx or Common Genet.

Sex ratio of nestlings

Because of the overlap in size between male and female Red Kites, there is no entirely reliable method of sexing live birds other than by analysing the DNA from blood samples. All the birds taken as nestlings in the early years of the reintroduction programme in Britain were sexed in this way, as were a proportion of wild-fledged birds in the establishing populations; 449 birds in total. Although these birds originated from a variety of different source countries, the overall totals of 226 males and 223 females seems to confirm the expected 1:1 sex ratio that has been found in most bird of prey species that have been studied.

Human disturbance

The Red Kite is relatively tolerant of routine human activity away from the immediate area of the nest, and breeding territories are sometimes located close to busy roads, farmsteads and public footpaths. In these situations, the birds quickly learn to ignore routine comings and goings within sight of the nest. They are much less tolerant of human intrusion close to the nest itself and even unwitting disturbance of this kind can cause problems.

Adults often perform a very characteristic display-flight if someone approaches the nest area. It involves flying in fairly tight circles, often directly above the intruder, with exaggerated, deep flapping and a series of highly distinctive, rapid, flicked wing-beats as the bird changes direction. This behaviour is usually only observed close to a nest site and often, although not always, when only a single bird is present in the air. It probably serves as a form of communication between members of the pair; a means by which the bird near the nest can signal to the other adult away foraging, warning of the disturbance and encouraging a swift return. The rapid arrival of the second bird of the pair on several occasions when this display was observed at nests in central England adds weight to this explanation. It is possible that this display could also function as a signal to the intruder, showing that they have been spotted, and carrying the threat of attack, even if this is unlikely to be put into practice.

Human disturbance is potentially most damaging when Red Kites have eggs or small chicks which can rapidly become chilled if the adults are kept off the nest, particularly in poor weather. They are also vulnerable to predation if the adults are distracted by intruders in the nest area. Early on in the breeding season there is a risk that the pair may even desert a nest site completely if disturbance is frequent. In Britain, forestry operations close to a nest site are a frequently reported source of disturbance. It is recommended, as first suggested for Goshawks (Petty 1989), that such activities are not carried out within about 400m of an active nest during the breeding season.

The behavioural response of adult Red Kites to human disturbance close to the nest varies considerably. Based on the experience of fieldworkers, it is believed that the female tends to be the more demonstrative of the pair when the nest is disturbed although the lack of a noticeable size difference between the two sexes makes this difficult to confirm. Some birds remain silent and limit their protestations to high circling above the nest area, including the wing-flicking display referred to above. Others circle very low overhead and call repeatedly for as long as the disturbance continues. Nests in Britain are often visited when the chicks are well-grown in order to fit rings and wing-tags. As the nest tree is climbed an adult will often circle low over the trees, sometimes even passing below the level of the canopy. On one occasion in southern England, the tree climber received a considerable shock when he was actually struck on the back by a particularly persistent bird. At another site, Nigel Snell of the Southern England Kite Group, was watching the nest tree being climbed when he was struck on the back of the head. Yarrell (1857) was in no doubt that Red Kites sometimes vigorously defended their nests, citing the example of a boy who climbed to a nest and received not only a severely wounded hand but also a hole in his hat before he could drive away the parent bird. Thankfully, such incidents are extremely unusual.

Well-grown nestlings usually lie flat on the nest platform when there is disturbance near to the nest and can then be virtually impossible to see from the ground. If young are within a week or so of fledging age when the nest is visited then there is a danger of premature fledging. This is a behavioural response seen in many species and has evolved to give young birds at least a chance of survival if a predator reaches the nest, threatening them with almost certain death unless they can escape. It is important that nest visits are timed to avoid this period as the young have a higher chance of survival if they are left to fledge when fully ready for their first flight.

When the chicks are handled by fieldworkers they tend to play dead and rarely put up any kind of struggle when rings or wing-tags are being fitted. This is in contrast to the more feisty behaviour seen in the young of many other birds of prey and no doubt reflects the lack of strength and power that young Red Kites possess. With weak talons designed for a life of scavenging rather than active hunting, the best bet for surviving an encounter with a predator (which is how handling by humans is no doubt interpreted) is not to fight back but to remain lifeless and hope that the predator loses interest. Occasionally the young do make half-hearted attempts to struggle and can inflict minor wounds to the hand with their claws. It is often the smallest chick in the brood that is the least cooperative when it comes to being handled, perhaps because they have become used to defending themselves in the nest during attacks from larger siblings.

In Britain the Red Kite is listed on Schedule 1 of The Wildlife and Countryside Act (1981), making it illegal to disturb birds at, or near to, an active nest without a licence. This protection extends from the early season when the nest is being built, through until the young are fully independent of their parents.

Breeding productivity

In most of the Red Kite's range, successful pairs fledge between one and four chicks with an overall average, for pairs that reach the egg-laying stage, of about 1.5-2 fledged young for each breeding attempt (Table 13). As in all long-lived birds, there is considerable variation in breeding success between individual pairs breeding in the same area. One of the most successful breeding pairs in northern Scotland has reared an average of three chicks each year, resulting in 21 young being fledged in just seven years. In contrast, another pair has bred in the same area for 11 consecutive years but reared only 13 young in that time. In mid-Wales, productivity is significantly lower than elsewhere in Britain. A maximum of three chicks are reared and, on average, less than one chick fledges for each breeding attempt, although productivity has improved slightly in recent decades (see below). Productivity in southern Europe is generally lower than in populations further north with, for example, only 0.8 young fledging per breeding attempt, on average, in the south of Spain. Even in Corsica, where the population has shown an increase in recent years, productivity is relatively low at 1.3 fledged young per breeding pair. This may reflect the fact that the hot, dry Mediterranean lowlands do not provide the most suitable conditions for breeding Red Kites (see Chapter 7).

In Table 14, the high proportion of broods of two or three young in England and Scotland contrasts markedly with the situation in Wales, where a single chick is by far the most common brood-size and only 4% of nests fledge three

155

Table 13: **Breeding productivity of Red Kites in Europe**

Area	Years	Young fledged per breeding (egg-laying) pair	Source of information
Southern England	1990s	2.0 (n=292)	Southern England Kite Group
Central England	1996-03	1.8 (n=90)	English Nature/Forest Enterprise
Yorkshire	2002-06	1.8 (n=123)	Doug Simpson (pers. comm.)
Central Scotland	1998-02	1.7 (n=39)	Orr-Ewing *et al.* (2006)
Northern Scotland	1992-03	2.1 (n=257)	Scottish Ornithologists' Club (2003)
Wales	1951-80	0.6 (n=571)	Cross & Davis (2005)
	1981-99	0.9 (n=1574)	Cross & Davis (2005)
Sweden	1980s-90s	1.7 (n=1443)	Kjellén (1996)
Eastern Germany	1980s	1.8 (n=491)	Evans & Pienkowski (1991)
Northeast France	1971-82	1.4 (n=55)	Mougeot & Bretagnolle (2006)
Switzerland	1995-03	1.7 (n=368)	Mougeot & Bretagnolle (2006)
Corsica	1996-99	1.3 (n=217)	Mougeot & Bretagnolle (2006)
Southern Spain	1989-00	0.8 (n=208)	Sergio *et al.* (2005)

young. Various reasons have been suggested for the poor breeding performance in Wales including the effects of inbreeding, an unsuitable climate, food shortage resulting from the unproductive nature of the land, and interspecific competition with Buzzards and Ravens. Each of these factors is discussed in more detail under the headings below.

Inbreeding

There is clear evidence from DNA analysis of blood samples that Welsh Red Kites show significantly less genetic variation than Red Kites from continental Europe (May *et al.* 1993b). This is the result of the genetic bottleneck that occurred when the Welsh population was reduced to a very low level in the first half of the 20th century. There is much greater genetic variation in Red Kite populations in France, Spain and Germany, as numbers there were not reduced to the same extent (Roques & Negro 2005). It has been suggested that the relatively high proportion of unhatched eggs found in Welsh nests results from a high level of inbreeding-related infertility (Cross & Davis 2005). However, other factors

Table 14: **Red Kite brood sizes at, or near, fledging in England, Wales and Scotland**
Welsh data: 1946-2004 (Cross & Davis 2005); English data: 1995-2000 (Southern England Kite Group/English Nature/RSPB; unpublished reports); Scottish data: 1990s (RSPB/Scottish Natural Heritage)

Brood size	Number of broods (% of brood size for each country)		
	Wales	**Scotland**	**England**
1	1160 (63)	25 (20)	53 (17)
2	600 (33)	45 (36)	146 (46)
3	64 (4)	53 (42)	113 (35)
4	0 (0)	3 (2)	5 (2)

such as poor food supply, and hence poor condition of the breeding adults before laying, could also be responsible. Work carried out by Nick Fox using artificial incubation, has now shown that, although some pairs do consistently produce infertile eggs, the majority of Welsh eggs are fertile and capable of producing young.

May *et al.* (1993b) provide two lines of evidence to suggest that inbreeding is not the most important factor in reducing productivity in Wales. Firstly, a sub-population in the south of the Welsh breeding range showed even lower levels of genetic variation than is typical, but had significantly higher productivity than birds in the rest of the range. Secondly, blood samples taken from Swedish Red Kites, where the population was also reduced to a low level, revealed similar levels of inbreeding to the Welsh population (although the sample size was small) and yet productivity is relatively high (Table 13). This evidence does not entirely rule out a negative effect due to inbreeding but does suggest that there are other factors of equal or greater importance. It will only be possible to determine with certainty whether inbreeding has a negative effect on productivity if, in the future, inbred Welsh birds are found breeding in the same areas as the more genetically varied reintroduced Red Kites. Productivity levels could then be compared in isolation from other factors relating to the currently separate breeding areas.

Competition with other species

A review of the diet of Red Kite, Buzzard and Raven suggests that there will inevitably be a certain amount of competition between the three species (Tubbs

1974, Ratcliffe 1997). Buzzards and Ravens both take carrion regularly and Buzzards hunt for small mammals that are also taken by Red Kites. Buzzards occur in all the Red Kite areas in Britain but densities are highest in mid-Wales. Ravens are scarce in central and southern England and in the Scottish Red Kite areas, but are very common in mid-Wales. Although the reintroduced Red Kite populations may benefit from reduced levels of competition for food with these species, other carrion feeders such as Carrion/Hooded Crows and Magpies are common throughout Britain. Elsewhere in Europe, Red Kites also face competition from these species, albeit, in the case of Buzzards and Ravens, at lower densities than are found in mid-Wales (Hagemeijer & Blair 1997).

Competition has also been suggested as a reason for the low productivity of Red Kites in southern Spain, in this case, with the migratory Black Kite which is very common here. Veiga and Hiraldo (1990) found that the diets of the two species in the Doñana National Park were similar although there was some partitioning of foraging areas, with Red Kites hunting more in areas of scrub and Black Kites spending more time in marshland habitats. Viñuela et al. (1999) believed that competition with Black Kites could be adversely affecting both the density and productivity of Red Kites in Doñana and there have even been calls for a local cull of Black Kites in order to help stem the decline in the endangered Red Kite population within the National Park (Sergio et al. 2005).

Climate

Cross and Davis (2005) attributed 6% of nest failures in Wales to wet weather and a further 18% of failures occurred around the time of hatching when young are at their most vulnerable to adverse weather conditions. Small, downy chicks quickly become chilled when wet, especially when temperatures are low, and the cool, damp weather that is frequent in mid-Wales in the spring is far from ideal for rearing young. Such conditions also have an indirect effect on the abundance of prey species, and persistent rain restricts the hunting efforts of adults, meaning that less food is brought to the nest. As a result, one of the best times to watch Red Kites is during a dry spell on an otherwise wet day, or on the first dry day following several rainy days. During these times the birds are often very active, keen to make the most of the opportunity to find food, having been restricted by the previous poor conditions.

Land productivity and food supply

The majority of the Red Kite breeding range in mid-Wales is dominated by rock types that yield relatively infertile soils and which therefore support a rather low diversity and abundance of animal life. A sub-population that has become established in southern Wales occurs in an area with a more fertile substrate which sustains a higher diversity and abundance of potential prey species (May *et al.* 1993b). In this area, a significantly higher proportion of territorial pairs initiate breeding and a higher proportion of pairs are successful in rearing young to fledging (81.5%, n=54 against 55.7%, n=235). The noticeable improvement in breeding productivity in Wales during the last decade (see Table 13) is mainly a result of the spread of birds into this more productive area.

Even in successful nests in mid-Wales, the majority of pairs fledge only a single chick, despite the fact that more than one egg often hatches. This points strongly towards an impoverished food supply as an important factor influencing breeding success and is backed up by RSPB research showing that, where two or more chicks are present, the oldest bird sometimes kills its smaller sibling if food is in short supply (Lovegrove *et al.* 1990).

A shortage of food may be the underlying reason behind breeding failures attributed to other causes. Chicks, for example, are more vulnerable to predation and to chilling in poor weather if the adults are forced to spend long periods away from the nest in order to find food. The risk of disease is also higher if chicks are malnourished as a result of a poor food supply. Lovegrove (1990) suggested that chick deaths from *Salmonella* and *Escherichia coli* bacteria in Wales were more likely when the adults brought in putrefying meat, in the absence of other, more suitable, food. The high proportion of unhatched eggs found in Welsh nests could be related to the condition of the breeding female at the time of laying, which again, is dependent on food supply. This has been shown to be the case in studies of several other birds of prey, including the Buzzard, where the proportion of addled eggs in a population was lower in years with a good food supply (Newton 1979).

Breeding density

In England, active Red Kite nests are sometimes found within 100m of each other (e.g. Evans *et al.* 1999) and, in such cases, the defended area around the nest is clearly very small. In 2000, the southern England breeding area supported approximately 0.25 pairs/km^2, with a density of 0.58 pairs/km^2 in the central 100km^2 core of the range (Wotton *et al.* 2002). One nest had no fewer than eight neighbouring nests within a 1km radius. Although monitoring has not been as intensive in subsequent years, there is little doubt that densities are now even higher than this. Typical densities in Wales are far lower, although there are aggregations of pairs in certain areas and active nests have been found only 200m apart in the same season.

In the northern Harz foothills in north-eastern Germany, densities of 0.3-0.5 pairs/km^2 have been recorded over a wide area and, in 1979, an incredible 136 pairs were counted in the 13km^2 Hakel Forest in this region (Hagemeijer & Blair 1997). The density of over 10 pairs/km^2 in this forest gives a somewhat false impression of the true abundance of Red Kites in the area as nests were concentrated in a central forest with birds foraging over a considerably greater area of surrounding farmland. In recent years, this population has become more dispersed with a higher number of pairs breeding in small belts of poplars and even isolated trees in the open countryside, and far fewer in the main forest. In Spain, a breeding survey found an average of 0.03 pairs/km^2 across large parts

Table 15: **Breeding densities of Red Kites in Europe**

Area and years	Pairs/km^2 (number of breeding pairs)	Source and further details
Chiltern Hills, southern England (2000)	0.58 (58)	Wotton *et al.* (2002): Figure is for the highest density 10km by 10km square in core of breeding range
Black Isle, northern Scotland (2000)	0.09 (9)	Wotton *et al.* (2002): Figure is for the highest density 10km by 10km square in core of breeding range
Mid-Wales (2000)	0.18 (18)	Wotton *et al.* (2002): Figure is for the highest density 10km by 10km square in Wales. Average density throughout the Welsh range was only 0.03 pairs/km^2
Harz mountains, eastern Germany (1991)	0.49 (730)	Hagemeijer & Blair (1997): Much higher densities of up to 10.4 pairs/km^2 in one core forest area
Spain (1994)	0.03-0.16	Viñuela *et al.* (1999): National survey found a small proportion of 10km by 10km squares with >0.16 pairs/km^2, mainly in central Spain
Doñana National Park, southern Spain (1989-2000)	0.32 (20)	Sergio *et al.* (2005): Small, high density population but low productivity, possibly limited by competition with Black Kites
Corsica (1997)	1.8 (75)	Mougeot & Bretagnolle (2006): Density quoted is from the core study area of 42km^2. Density is much lower for breeding areas in Corsica as a whole

of the country and only very limited areas supported more than 0.16 pairs/km^2 (Viñuela *et al*. 1999). As in the Hakel Forest, local densities were sometimes much higher as a result of the grouping of nests in isolated blocks of suitable breeding habitat.

High densities of Red Kites breeding in a small area can suggest that birds are aggregating into loose colonies as occurs in the closely-related Black Kite. However, at times, as with the Hakel Forest example, high breeding densities simply reflect the patchiness of available breeding habitat, with only certain areas of countryside having suitable woodland in which the birds can nest, in close proximity to a good food supply. High densities can also result from the fact that Red Kites show a high degree of natal philopatry, with young birds tending to return to close to the site where they were reared, when they are old enough to breed, rather than establishing territories in areas well away from other Red Kites (see Chapter 10). It is unlikely that Red Kites are genuinely semi-colonial in the sense that they derive any specific benefits from aggregating into high-density breeding groups, although this has been suggested by some. Mougeot and Bretagnolle (2006), for example, noted that the most frequent inter-nest distance of birds in Corsica was only 250m and believed that Red Kites sometimes aggregated into loose colonies of between 3-12 pairs. If this is the case then a possible advantage of breeding close to other pairs is the ability to learn about potential food sources from observing other adults in the same area (see under 'Network foraging' in Chapter 9). This may be the primary reason for the pattern of semi-colonial nesting often found in the Black Kite (Bustamante & Hiraldo 1993). However, a clear disadvantage of breeding at high density is the increased level of competition for limited food resources from other adults. Snell *et al*. (2002) found that as the population within a 2.5km radius of the release site in southern England increased from six to 21 pairs between 1995 and 2000, average productivity declined from 2.3 to 1.6 young per pair, presumably reflecting difficulties in finding sufficient food for nestlings. It is perhaps for this reason that the most commonly found pattern is for Red Kite nests to be well spaced within the occupied breeding range, as far as is allowed by the availability of suitable nesting habitat.

Chapter 9

SOCIAL BEHAVIOUR

Many birds of prey are gregarious, particularly outside the breeding season, but the Red Kite, its close relative the Black Kite and several of the vultures, take this behaviour to extremes. Throughout the Red Kite's range, communal winter roosting is typical and the majority of birds across a large area may use the same roost site each evening. In areas with a healthy resident or wintering population, gatherings of several hundred birds are not uncommon, forming one of the most impressive wildlife spectacles in Europe. It is likely that birds benefit from communal gatherings through being able to forage in loose groups the following day. Roosts may also serve as a place to interact with potential future mates. There is often a significant amount of social interaction between birds gathering at roost sites and this includes behaviour which is best described as play, as it seems to serve no other useful purpose. On evenings when there is a breeze, and so flight is effortless, spectacular aerial chases take place, with birds diving at each other and sometimes almost interlocking talons in mock fights before separating again.

The communal roost

The social nature of the Red Kite is best appreciated by visiting a major communal roost site on a winter's afternoon. During the latter part of the afternoon a slow trickle of birds gradually increases until single birds and small groups are arriving almost constantly from all directions. Initially, birds can be seen over a wide area but they are increasingly drawn together, either perching in groups in prominent trees along a hedgerow or at the edge of the roost wood, or wheeling and chasing together over the roost area. New arrivals are frequently greeted by calling from, particularly adult, birds that are already present. This, together with the aerial activity, may help to draw more birds towards the roost, as has been recorded in communally-roosting Ravens (Marzluff *et al*. 1996). All this activity is loosely termed 'pre-roosting' and many individuals do not move to their final resting place for the night, usually well within a woodland and out of sight, until the light is beginning to fade. Some late arrivals even slip into the roost wood when it is almost completely dark.

Patterns of behaviour during pre-roost gatherings are strongly influenced by the weather. Aerial activity, for example, is greatly increased when there is a moderate to strong wind, as the birds are able to fly more efficiently, with less expenditure of energy. On calm afternoons, birds arriving in the roost area are more likely to remain perched in prominent trees for long periods. Here, they often spend time preening and can sometimes be seen pecking at their feet to dislodge caked soil picked up from landing in muddy fields. It appears that there is also less aerial activity on very cold evenings, presumably to avoid excessive heat loss when flying through cold air. However, because the coldest winter days tend to occur when there is little or no wind, it is difficult to distinguish between the influence of these two factors.

The attendance patterns of individual birds vary, probably depending at least partly on foraging success during the day. Birds arriving at the roost in near darkness are likely to be those that have struggled to find food and have made the most of all available daylight in order to continue foraging. The bulging crop of some of the birds arriving in the roost area in daylight, clearly visible as they pass overhead, shows that they have fed recently.

Once most birds are settled in their final roosting position as dusk approaches, there is a significant reduction in visible activity. The late arrivals often head directly into the roost wood as there is little daylight left in which to indulge in the usual pre-roosting activities. At this stage, perched birds are sensitive to disturbance within, or close to, the roost wood. They will usually tolerate someone walking quietly, even close to the edge of the wood, but someone entering the wood or a sudden, unexpected, loud noise can send them all back up into the air.

On one memorable clear and still early evening at a roost site in southern England, just as the sun was finally disappearing behind the low Chiltern hills, a loud clattering noise from a nearby farmyard disturbed upwards of 100 Red Kites from their perches within a small wood in the valley below. They rose above the wood with a heavy, flapping flight, initially in a tight group, but gradually fanning out over a wider area of the surrounding countryside, before returning, in small groups, to resettle in trees close to the original roost. The maximum recorded count at this site is no fewer than 217 birds (Snell *et al.* 2002). In central England, disturbance caused by pigeon shooting or deer stalking late in the afternoon has resulted in a sudden change of the final roosting location as all the gathered birds have flown up and drifted several hundred metres to a different group of trees. At this site, the birds have a number of alternative blocks of woodland that are regularly used for roosting, all within an area of about 2km^2. The final selection on each evening is, at times, governed by disturbance factors, but often seems to be random. The location chosen by the first few birds to settle is probably simply copied by later arrivals.

When birds are disturbed into the air en masse, this provides a valuable opportunity to undertake a count of the number of birds using the roost site. Counts of up to 500 birds have been made in this way at Spanish roosts (Viñuela 1997). At sites where disturbance is unusual, 'flush' counts can be made by having people deliberately enter the wood as the light is fading, with observers posted at surrounding vantage points to count the birds that fly up (Carter & Grice 2002). It is, of course, imperative that counts of this type are undertaken only on rare occasions and by individuals closely involved in monitoring the local population, in order to ensure that the birds are not disturbed excessively (Carter & Grice 2002, Hardy *et al.* 2006).

A rather unexpected behaviour has been recorded in roosting birds in the Chilterns using radio-tracking. Peter Stevens, from the Southern England Kite Group, used radio-receivers with computer loggers at major winter roosts in order to automatically record the presence of radio-tagged birds. On several occasions, the radio-signal from a bird was lost from one logger in the middle of the night, only to be picked up soon afterwards by a logger at another nearby roost. For whatever reason, possibly human disturbance, birds were moving from one roost to another in complete darkness. This behaviour has also been recorded in communally roosting Ravens in the north-eastern United States though, here too, without a fully satisfactory explanation for why it occurs (Marzluff *et al*. 1996).

Departures from roost sites in the morning follow a similar pattern to arrivals, with single birds and small groups leaving at intervals from first light onwards. The birds that leave soon after first light may be those that struggled to find food during the previous day and are therefore keen to resume foraging at the earliest opportunity. As in the evening, birds leaving the roost sometimes call to each other as they head off to begin foraging. Continuous rain or dense fog tends to prolong the period spent in the roost area as such conditions are far from ideal for active foraging. If the wet or foggy weather persists then some birds may remain in, or close to, the roost for the whole day.

In many Red Kite areas the requirement for an area of woodland not subject to frequent human disturbance is satisfied by a large number of different sites, and it is not known why particular woods are selected as roosts and then used repeatedly for many years. Such sites perhaps become established as traditional roosts through birds in each generation simply following the example of older birds that are already familiar with the location. In central England, the first birds released at the start of the reintroduction project in 1995 quickly settled on a roost site about 8km away from the release pens. Radio-tracking and direct observation showed that the same area of woodland was used for roosting every night throughout the winter and, in subsequent years, each new group of released and, more recently, wild-fledged, young have come to use the same roost. Counts in excess of 50 birds were made regularly at this site in the late 1990s and early 2000s. The site remains in use today although there are now a number of different roosts in regular use as the population has increased. In southern England, where the population is now well over 1,000 birds, there are many different roost sites and radio-tracking work has shown that birds often move between sites during the winter, rather than remaining faithful to one or two roosts (Dixon 2001, Peter Stevens pers. comm.). Radio-tracking has revealed a similar pattern of behaviour in southern Spain where wintering birds from central Europe utilise numerous different roost sites during the course of a winter (Heredia *et al*. 1991).

The distance between active roosts varies with local population density and, to a lesser extent, with time of year. In central Spain, the distance between adjacent roost sites varied from 3.6km to 10km in areas with high numbers of wintering birds, and there was evidence that birds tended to concentrate in fewer, larger, roosts later in the winter (Viñuela 1992). In Britain, roosts are usually more fragmented and used less predictably in autumn and early winter, with numbers at the most important sites building up from August-September to a peak in the November-February period. Roosts generally begin to break up from about mid-February as birds start to move away to potential breeding sites. Communal gatherings of young, non-breeding, birds occur throughout the spring and summer but these are not as large, predictable or site-faithful as is the case in winter.

Composition of roost gatherings

In the reintroduced populations in England and Scotland, some established pairs remain on their breeding territories throughout the winter and are only seen infrequently at communal pre-roost gatherings. Other pairs attend the roosts regularly, although visits tend to become less frequent in late winter when they begin to spend more time close to their breeding site. The pair-bond is clearly maintained throughout the winter in at least a proportion of adults that regularly join communal roosts and paired birds, identifiable from their wing-tags, often arrive at the roost together. Many roosts are dominated by first-year and second-year birds which have yet to make their first breeding attempt and therefore have no ties to a breeding site. In Wales, there is a similar pattern, with many of the larger roosts dominated by immature birds and adults often roosting close to their nest sites. Davis *et al.* (2001) suggested that some small roosts, involving mainly adults, were made up of birds from breeding pairs in the immediate area. These seldom supported more than 12 birds, in contrast to roosts dominated by immature birds which could involve up to 50-60 individuals.

In southern Spain, Heredia *et al.* (1991) used radio-tracking to highlight differences in roosting behaviour between wintering birds from central Europe and the resident breeding population. Wintering Red Kites (both adults and first-years) gathered at communal roosts of 5-80 individuals, where they were sometimes joined by immature birds from the resident population. In contrast, the resident breeding adults almost always roosted in their nest tree or its immediate vicinity. Radio-tracking of a breeding pair in Germany also showed that the birds spent the majority of nights in winter roosting close to their breeding site (Nachtigall *et al.* 2003).

Network foraging

One of the main potential benefits of joining a communal roost is the chance to improve foraging efficiency by learning about new food sources from other birds. The 'information centre' theory (Ward & Zahavi 1973) suggests that birds

Pre-roosting Red Kites typically perch facing into the wind to avoid their feathers being unduly ruffled

are able to improve their chance of finding food by following other, more knowledgeable, individuals from a roost or colony. This has been shown to occur in only a very small number of bird species, including the Raven and American Black Vulture (Marzluff *et al*. 1996, Buckley 1997). In winter, Red Kites frequently feed on mammal or bird carcasses that are large enough to provide food for several individuals and may remain as a suitable food source for several days. In theory, it would therefore be possible for an individual that has struggled to find food, to follow a more successful bird from the roost on the following day in order to locate a carcass at which to feed.

In order to test the information centre theory, Hiraldo *et al*. (1993) studied a group of radio-tagged Red Kites and their foraging behaviour in southern Spain. They found that, although Red Kites fed at carcasses large enough to be shared, in this area these usually lasted for only a single day and following successful birds from the roost was therefore unlikely to lead directly to a known food source. This was backed up by observations of birds departing from the roost in the morning. The birds often left the roost in small groups, but there appeared to be no obvious leader and individuals known to have fed well during the previous day were not followed. This study suggested that an alternative food finding strategy termed 'network foraging' (Mock *et al*. 1988) fitted the observed patterns of behaviour more convincingly and provided a valid explanation of why communal roosting was beneficial. According to this theory, it is worthwhile for a bird to leave the roost as part of a loose group so that when one individual is successful in locating a new food source, the others in the group can quickly converge to share in the discovery. Each bird in the group effectively improves its chances of finding food and, as carcasses are often large enough to feed several birds, there is little disadvantage to the finder in having to share. As discussed in Chapter 6, the rapid arrival of a group of birds at a food source may even be advantageous to the finder as Red Kites are cautious about landing on the ground to feed. The presence of other birds provides an element of 'safety in numbers' with additional pairs of eyes to look for potential danger. Gathering at communal roosts is thus advantageous as it ensures that sufficient birds are available at the start of each day for social foraging of this nature to be possible.

Casual observations of Red Kites in Britain certainly suggest that social foraging does take place, with birds sometimes locating potential food sources by watching other Red Kites (as well as other scavenging birds such as Buzzards and corvids). From a distance, a bird on the lookout for food is much more likely to be able to see another scavenging bird on the ground, or circling low over the area, than the animal carcass itself, and the effect is enhanced once a small group of birds is present. It clearly makes sense for hungry Red Kites to keep an eye on each other (and other scavengers) as well as scanning the ground below for food.

It is not clear to what extent network foraging takes place in the breeding season. The need for smaller, non-shareable, food items that can be carried back to the nest means that, if it does occur, it is likely to be far less important than in winter. Nevertheless, Red Kites sometimes nest at high density and do not defend exclusive territories, so it is likely that breeding adults do, to some extent, learn about food sources by keeping an eye on other birds in the area.

Other benefits of communal roosting

Roosting in groups may result in additional benefits, unrelated to social foraging. Some species are known to conserve heat by roosting in numbers. Small passerines, with their high surface-area to volume ratio, are particularly vulnerable to cold winter conditions and often roost huddled together for warmth. Larger birds rarely roost together for this purpose, at least in temperate climates, and it is highly unlikely that the Red Kite is an exception to this rule. In central England, when roosts were visited on moonlit nights, groups of birds could be seen perched close together in several different trees but not in such close proximity as to suggest they were trying to conserve heat (Ottway 2002).

Many birds roost and forage in flocks in order to reduce the risk of predation. With more pairs of eyes there is a better chance that approaching predators will be detected and the chance of a successful attack is reduced. It is hard to believe that full-grown Red Kites are sufficiently vulnerable to predators when roosting to make communal gatherings worthwhile for this purpose and adult Red Kites that roost solitarily, together with many other solitary roosting raptors, do not seem to suffer significant losses. The anti-predator explanation for communal roosting is perhaps more appropriate for ground-roosting species such as harriers, where there is significant danger from ground predators and benefits from social foraging are less likely to be important (e.g. Clarke 1996).

For a species that normally pairs for life, finding an appropriate mate is clearly very important. Other species are thought to pair up when in non-breeding flocks, for example the Magpie (Birkhead 1991), and if this is the case in Red Kites, then the communal roost no doubt provides the best opportunity. Aerial displays involving two first-year birds are frequently seen during pre-roost gatherings and it is possible that these sometimes involve a male and female in the early stages of pair-bonding. One highly distinctive display involves two birds flying close together, one behind the other, with both using exaggerated deep, slow, wing-beats. In the breeding season, this same display between adults has been interpreted as essentially aggressive as it is sometimes followed by a rapid chase, but it may also have a role in strengthening the bond between paired birds. Radio-tracking of immature birds at roosts in southern England has provided some evidence that pair bonds do begin to form at communal roosts. Dixon (2001) found that a pair of birds that bred for the first time in 2001 spent a higher proportion of nights together at the same roost during the previous winter than they did with other radio-tagged immature birds. In the same study he also found that the average number of nights spent at a roost before changing to an alternative roost was significantly lower for second-year birds than for birds in their first year. Second-year birds are likely to breed in the following spring and a possible explanation for their higher frequency of roost switching is that it facilitates mixing with a higher number of individual Red Kites and hence a greater opportunity to find a suitable mate. It is unlikely that Red Kite roosts form primarily to facilitate pairing but, once established, it is inevitable that unpaired birds will mix and they no doubt make the most of the opportunity.

Social behaviour and distribution

The Red Kite's distribution across its European range is noticeably patchy, with pockets of high density close to areas where they are seen only infrequently. The reasons for this include differences in habitat suitability, food supply and the intensity of persecution but, at times, these explanations do not seem entirely adequate. Areas with few Red Kites sometimes have a very similar landscape and management regime to an adjacent area supporting a substantial population.

Although persecution is usually the main factor responsible for fragmenting populations in the first place, the highly social nature of the Red Kite tends to reduce the rate at which areas now free from such threats can be recolonised. Young birds in their first winter are reluctant to move away from areas where Red Kites are common, as they would then be unable to benefit from group foraging and the other benefits that derive from social interactions at communal roosts (Carter 2003). As a result, traditional roosts tend to increase in size until the amount of food available locally imposes an upper limit on numbers and birds are then forced to explore further afield. When birds do disperse in their first winter, they invariably join up with Red Kites in other areas rather than settling in vacant habitat. There is a similar tendency to settle at a breeding site in an area where Red Kites are already present (see Chapter 10) and this too acts as a brake on range expansion.

Play

The concept of play activity as a means of learning or improving skills is a familiar one in the mammal world but there are far fewer documented examples involving birds. Nevertheless, there is every reason to suppose that the benefits of play are much the same for both groups. A clue to this learning role for play in Red Kites is the prevalence of such activity in immature birds. Many of the examples described below involved young birds, yet to make their first breeding attempt. The same pattern is found in mammals where it is the young and inexperienced individuals that most commonly indulge in play, as a means of learning behaviour important in later adult life.

Two main forms of play activity are seen frequently in Red Kites, each with a number of variations on a similar theme. The first involves using outstretched talons to snatch at objects or vegetation in flight. This behaviour has been observed on a number of occasions at the main communal roost in central England, involving individual birds snatching foliage both from near to ground level and from the thin upper branches of deciduous trees. On one winter evening, a single bird was watched flying low above a crop of oilseed rape and grabbing at the leaves of the crop, only a few inches from the ground. The behaviour was repeated several times, with the leaves grabbed and then dropped fairly rapidly on each occasion. At the same site, birds were observed snatching foliage from the outer branches of trees, repeatedly dropping and re-catching the same leafy twig in flight. Each time the twig was dropped, the bird folded back its wings in order to lose height rapidly, enabling it to catch it again with ease.

Red Kites are often seen picking up objects from the ground and flying with them for a short period before dropping, and sometimes re-catching, them again. On some occasions, this is no doubt a genuine attempt to detect food and the object is quickly discarded as soon as the bird realises that it is inedible. At other times, such behaviour can only be regarded as play as the same object, clearly of no food value, is repeatedly picked up and dropped. If other Red Kites are nearby they often join in with the game, chasing each other and intercepting the object in mid-air if it is dropped by the leading bird. Encalado (1998) watched several Red Kites at a rubbish dump in Zamora, Spain playing with a piece of newspaper. A pursuing bird managed to snatch the paper from the talons of the initial owner and was, itself, then immediately chased by two other birds. In central England, dried sheep droppings are a favoured play object and other materials have included wool, sticks and feathers, as well as pieces of plastic and rubber. Sticks are sometimes carried by first-year, non-breeding birds in spring and this can lead to erroneous claims of nest building. They are, however, usually quickly dropped rather than carried away to a nest site.

The second main form of play activity involves aerial chases and mock fights between two or more birds. This is regularly seen at pre-roost gatherings, particularly on breezy days when the birds are able to use the wind to fly with minimal expenditure of energy. In central England, up to 70 birds have been watched circling together above the roost wood with frenetic chases between individuals occurring at regular intervals. Walters Davies and Davis (1973) coined the term 'circus' to describe such gatherings in Wales. Chases may develop into mock fights as one bird dives towards another with talons outstretched, and the other bird responds by rolling onto its back and thrusting out its own talons in defence. It sometimes appears as if the two birds must surely collide but direct contact is rare and the birds usually rejoin the circling group after only a brief bout of sparring. Where chases are more prolonged they frequently involve high-speed changes of direction as the leading bird twists and turns ahead of its pursuer with remarkable agility. This sort of interaction can be rather surprising if one is familiar with the Red Kite's usual leisurely, gliding flight as it drifts across open country in search of food.

Surprisingly, play can also extend to interactions with small aircraft including manned gliders, hang-gliders and even radio-controlled planes. One encounter with a motorised hang-glider in England involved both glider and bird out-climbing each other in turn, with both ending up at over 1,200 feet. Another involved five Red Kites following a radio-controlled glider and getting so close that the operator feared there would be a collision (Cocker & Mabey 2005). In the breeding season, gliders and other slow-flying small aircraft may be shadowed by Red Kites if they fly over a nest site and are interpreted by the birds as a potential threat. But at other times it appears to be curiosity and playfulness that leads to such encounters.

Both of the two main types of play observed in Red Kites have close parallels with forms of behaviour that are genuinely useful and it is easy to see how play could contribute to an individual's survival prospects by improving coordination or flying agility. Playing with objects, including the snatching of vegetation, could help to improve both foraging success and nest building skills. One of the Red Kite's most frequent foraging techniques involves flying down to grab an animal carcass or piece of carrion from the ground without pausing to land. This is clearly a difficult skill as birds sometimes swoop down and reach out with their talons, only to miss the intended target. Play no doubt helps birds to improve their success rate through repeated practice. Breeding is dependent on the collection of enough suitable nest material, either from the ground or, in some cases, sticks broken from a living tree. Here again, there are clear parallels with play involving objects, including sticks, seen in birds of pre-breeding age. Aerial

chases and mock fights in young birds are almost identical to behaviour used by breeding adults in order to defend the area around their nest site. Anything that improves agility must be of benefit in driving away a rival male or a potential nest predator, for example. Flying skills are also important in attracting a mate in the first place as display flights are thought to be an important part of courtship behaviour.

Interaction with corvids

Some of the aerial skills described above are of direct benefit when fending off unwelcome attention from corvids, an all too frequent activity for Red Kites in many areas. Most birds of prey are, at times, mobbed by corvids, but the Red Kite, with its slow, languid foraging flights, often low over the ground, is a particularly appealing target. Jackdaws, Rooks, Carrion/Hooded Crows and Magpies seem never to tire of the activity and sometimes a group of ten or more will gang up on an individual Red Kite, forming a long, straggling tail behind the hapless bird. If the harrying becomes too intense, the Red Kite may suddenly roll over in flight and turn towards the birds with talons outstretched, an action that usually has only a short-term effect and rarely prevents the mobbing birds from continuing with their harassment. A more successful strategy is simply to land in a tree and wait. The pursuing corvids often land in the same tree but must be careful not to stray within range of the bird's sharp talons and so the harrying stops, at least until it takes to the wing once more.

William Blundell, writing in the 17th century (quoted by Mitchell 1892), was well aware of the hostility between corvids and Red Kites, and how such behaviour could be exploited by those wishing to trap and kill Carrion Crows:

> [if you] take a Kite and a Carrion-Crow, and tie them down in the stubble with sufficient liberty, they will fight and cry in a strange manner: upon which there will come immediately great flocks of Crows from all parts, which, striking freely at the Kite, will many of them be taken in the lime twig which must be placed round in the stubble for that reason.

Mobbing birds no doubt view such a large bird of prey as a Red Kite as a potential threat, particularly in summer when they have nestlings or recently fledged young, and the act of mobbing is then a genuine attempt to drive the bird away from the area. At other times, they are more interested in the food that a bird is carrying and their behaviour is designed to cause sufficient inconvenience to encourage food to be dropped so that it can be stolen. However, corvids often mob a Red Kite that is not carrying food and, in attempting to retreat, is clearly signalling that it has no aggressive intentions. It is easy to believe that, in these situations, it is the corvids that are indulging in play activity, perhaps in preparation for the time when they have young, and sparring between the species becomes an altogether more serious business.

Chapter 10

HOME RANGE AND DISPERSAL

The size of the home range used during the breeding season and in winter, together with the tendency for young birds to disperse, varies across the Red Kite's range, influenced by factors such as climate, landscape and food supply. In high quality habitats in England and Scotland, where food is abundant and winters are mild, home ranges are generally small and adult birds may not stray far from their breeding site throughout the year. In resident populations, some birds remain in their natal area for their whole life, while others disperse during their first autumn or in the following spring, often travelling well away from their birthplace. Dispersal differs from migration in that it involves movements, mainly by first-year birds, which are exploratory in nature and unpredictable, with considerable variation in direction and distance travelled between individuals. Migration (covered in Chapter 4) involves regular, repeated, and, to a large extent, predictable, movements between separate breeding and wintering areas.

Home range

As Red Kites do not defend an exclusive feeding area from other Red Kites, even during the breeding season, 'home range', rather than 'territory', is the most appropriate term to describe the area they make use of. The focal point for the home range during the breeding season is the nest site, whilst in winter, adults either remain close to their breeding site or, particularly if food becomes more difficult to find, move to a more productive area. It is only possible to define home ranges accurately by carrying out intensive studies of birds fitted with radio-transmitters. In Britain most radio-tracking has involved first-year birds as radio-tags are fitted to nestlings before they fledge or to young birds released as part of the reintroduction programme, and they do not always last into adulthood.

Breeding season

The home range utilised by breeding pairs for foraging varies markedly with the local availability of food. In Wales, Walters Davies and Davis (1973) noted that individually-marked birds were occasionally recorded as far as 15km away from their nest. In Germany, Ortlieb (1989) thought that foraging flights of up to 10km from nests were typical and in southern Spain, Veiga and Hiraldo (1990) recorded feeding trips of up to 20km away from nests. These, however, represent extreme distances and breeding birds do the majority of foraging much closer to the nest site. Direct observations of the male bird from a breeding pair near Göttingen, central Germany, showed that the maximum distance travelled from the nest was 4.5km and the majority of foraging flights were within 2.5km of the nest (Porstendörfer 1997). Almost all flights were within an arc of approximately 180° on the eastern side of the nest site and the total home range in which the bird located food for itself and its nestlings was a relatively limited 7.5km².

Observations of wing-tagged birds from known breeding sites in Wales involved 30 records of birds 2-4km from their nest, one record at 5.5km and two records at 9km (Davis et al. 2001). Without exception, all these observations of birds more than 2km away from the nest site involved males. Females generally hunted within a few hundred metres of the nest, although they could be absent from the immediate vicinity of the nest once the young were well grown.

A similar pattern is apparent in England. Figure 7 is based on 51 records of wing-tagged birds seen at least 1km away from their nest sites during the breeding season in central England. As in Wales, females were not recorded more than 2km from the nest and were only very rarely seen more than 1km from their breeding site. Eight out of the nine records where birds were seen more than 4km from the nest involved the same male bird, in a year when he had moved 5km from his previous nest site. Despite this change of breeding site, he was regularly seen foraging over land close to the previous year's nest site, requiring longer flights from the nest than is usual. It was presumably advantageous for this bird to make use of foraging areas with which it was familiar from the previous year, despite the longer distance foraging flights required. What is less clear is why the breeding pair moved to a new nest site well away from a foraging area that was obviously so highly favoured. The main reason that adults forage close to the breeding site is that food for nestlings (and for the female when she is being fed by the male) must be carried back to the nest. Red Kites do not have the ability possessed by vultures, for example, to regurgitate food for the young and it is therefore not practical to range over large areas, well away from the nest.

Figure 7: **Foraging distances from nest sites in central England**

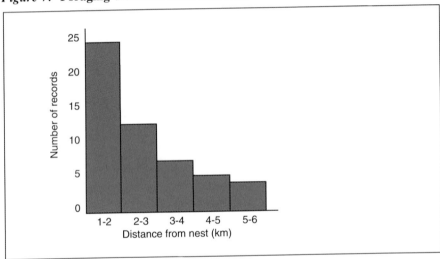

Within most Red Kite home ranges there will be habitats such as mature woodland and well-grown arable crops that are generally unsuitable for foraging. The area actually utilised by the pair will therefore be smaller than initially suggested by the total size of the home range based on sightings of birds. Radio-transmitters with a battery life of three years are now regularly being fitted to nestlings in Britain and elsewhere, and these should allow a more detailed assessment of the way in which breeding adults use habitats around their nest sites.

Winter

The communal roost becomes the focal point of the home range for many birds in winter, particularly for individuals that have yet to breed and for adults that winter away from their breeding site. Some individuals utilise a fairly restricted area around a single roost, returning every evening to the same site, whilst others wander more widely, visiting several different roosts and making use of a far larger area during the course of a winter. Because Red Kites do not defend an exclusive territory from other Red Kites, they are not restricted to a specific range with strict boundaries and are therefore able to exploit different areas opportunistically during the winter if patterns of food availability change. An intensive programme of Rabbit control on a particular farm, for example, may turn an area formerly lacking in animal carrion into a highly productive foraging area. Similarly, the beginning of the game-shooting season might provide a sudden abundance of carrion on estates where shooting is frequent, drawing in Red Kites from the surrounding countryside. In this respect, the Red Kite has a degree of flexibility that is not the case in more strictly territorial species such as the Buzzard, where most food is found within a defended area that may be smaller than 1km^2 (Tubbs 1974).

Radio-tracking of first-year Red Kites in central England over several winters showed that the majority of foraging took place within 4km of the single communal roost site used by all immature birds in the population (Carter & Grice 2000). Within this radius of the roost, some areas were used far more frequently than others, presumably according to the amount of food available. Home ranges determined for six individuals, based on at least 30 recorded locations for each bird, ranged from 19 to 32km^2, with an average of 23km^2. As is clear from the examples plotted in Figure 8, within each home range there are areas used more frequently than would be expected by chance. This is partly the result of local differences in food availability but is also influenced by the preferences of individual birds. The birds in Figure 8(a) and (b) clearly favoured an area to the northwest of the communal roost site, whereas the bird in 8(c) spent a much smaller proportion of its time in this area and was recorded more often to the south of the roost.

Winter home ranges were found to be rather more extensive in the Chilterns of southern England than in central England (Dixon 2001, pers. comm.). This was mainly because the larger, more established, population here no longer utilised only a single communal roost site. There were several major roosts and a number of smaller roosts spread over a relatively wide area. Radio-tracking showed that individual immature birds often made use of a number of different roosts during the course of a winter. Because they tended to forage in countryside

Figure 8: **Winter home ranges for three first-year Red Kites in central England, October-February, 1996-97** *(The background grid comprises 1km squares and each dot represents a location determined by radio-tracking)*

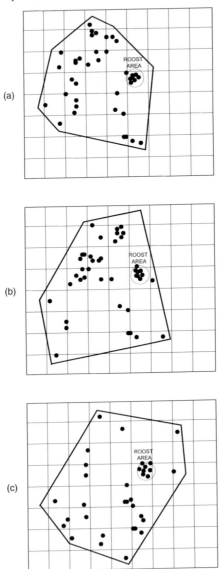

surrounding the roost where they spent the night, home ranges extended over a considerably larger area than if only a single roost had been used as in central England.

Adult Red Kites in Wales appear to adopt different patterns of behaviour depending on the nature of the breeding site (Davis *et al.* 2001). Some remain close to their nest sites throughout the year and make use of a relatively restricted home range in winter, similar to that used in the breeding season. Others move away from their nest site and range over a wider area, often visiting feeding sites in the company of large numbers of immature birds. Davis *et al.* (2001) thought that these birds were more likely to come from the less productive breeding sites, including those on higher ground, and that some movements were associated with the onset of a spell of cold weather. Wing-tagged first-year birds in Wales sometimes wander over very extensive areas as they are recorded at a number of widely-dispersed locations, especially feeding stations, during the course of a single winter.

In Doñana, southern Spain, there is a contrast in ranging behaviour between birds wintering in the area from breeding grounds in central Europe and the local resident adults (Heredia *et al.* 1991). A radio-tracking study showed that the resident adults used comparatively small home ranges in winter, centred on their nest sites where they returned to roost each night. Individual home ranges varied from 6.5 to 36km^2 with a median value for six different individuals of 29km^2. The core home ranges, defined as those areas used more frequently than would be expected by chance, varied from as little as 2.7 up to 11.5km^2, with a median value of 3.6km^2.

In the same area, wintering Red Kites from central Europe roosted communally and tended to utilise larger home ranges than the resident birds. The overall home ranges for a sample of eight birds varied from 15 to 42km^2 and core ranges varied from 4.3 to 14.5km^2, with a median value of 6km^2 (much higher than that of resident birds). As would be expected from the larger home ranges, wintering birds also tended to be found further away from their roost sites during the day, averaging 5.8km when located by radio-tracking, compared with an average of 3.9km for the resident birds. This clear difference in behaviour is probably a reflection of the greater knowledge of the local area by breeding adults with established home ranges. Through familiarity with a relatively small area around the nest site they are able to find sufficient food without resorting to social foraging. Wintering migrant birds do not enjoy such familiarity with their surroundings but can improve their chances of finding food by foraging over a larger area, often in loose groups.

Dispersive movements

Even in resident Red Kite populations a proportion of the young fledged each year undertake dispersive movements away from their natal area. These movements tend to be initiated in either the autumn, fairly soon after they have become independent, or in the following spring, and during the intervening winter period birds usually remain settled in the same area. In this respect the Red Kite differs from the closely related, but highly migratory, Black Kite, whose young move away from the nest almost as soon as they are independent (Bustamante & Hiraldo 1993). The dispersive movements made by young Red Kites are probably best viewed as exploratory in nature in that they provide birds with information on alternative areas that may influence where they settle when they are old enough to breed.

As shown in Table 16 and Figure 9, dispersive movements take place in all directions and, in some cases, over large distances. Studies of individually-marked birds in central and southern England have shown that although some birds disperse in autumn, a higher proportion of birds in these areas disperse in April and May when they are approximately one year old (Dixon 2001, Carter & Grice 2002) – See Table 4 in Chapter 4.

Arguably the most unexpected movement so far recorded involved a first-year Red Kite from the reintroduced population in northern Scotland. This individual fledged in July 1997 and was recorded in Iceland in December of the same year having undertaken a remarkable flight of more than 1,000km across the North Atlantic. Most large birds of prey avoid crossing expanses of water wherever possible, as the rising thermals used in order to gain height are much stronger over land. This individual may have become caught up in high-altitude winds that carried it north from Scotland, rather than deliberately setting out to fly in this direction. It survived two harsh Icelandic winters, helped by handouts of food from a local farmer, before being found covered in Fulmar oil and taken back to Scotland for rehabilitation. After a period of quarantine and convalescence, the bird was released back into the wild in northern Scotland in March 2000. The story did not ultimately have a happy ending as, six weeks later, it was found dead 42km away from the release point. The longest movement so far recorded involves a bird fledged in central Scotland that was found in its first autumn, 2,000km away near Porto in Portugal (see Table 16).

The majority of movements are not as extreme as the examples in Table 16 and, in resident populations, some young birds remain close to their natal site during their first year rather than dispersing. Many of the birds that do disperse, subsequently return to the area where they hatched (or were released) having been away for anything from a few days to almost two years. As would be

Table 16: Long distance movements of British Red Kites

Information for reintroduced populations from English Nature/Scottish Natural Heritage/RSPB project newsletters and reports. Welsh records from Welsh Kite Trust newsletters and Cross & Davis (1998)

Area of origin	Release (R) or fledging (F) date	Location and date recorded	Distance/direction travelled	Comments
Southern England	July 1990 (R)	15km NE of Rouen, France: January 1991	290km SE	Found dead after severe storms
Southern England	July 1993 (F)	Near Brussels, Belgium: December 1997	c.400km ESE	Found dead
Central England	July 1997 (R)	Near Holywell, north Wales: July 1997	200km WNW	Dead under powerlines only two weeks after being released. One of six birds released in central England to be recorded in Wales during their first winter, mostly associating with Welsh Red Kites
Central England	July 1997 (R)	Gouthwaite Reservoir, North Yorkshire: Oct–Dec 1997	210km NNW	Not recorded again after December 1997
Yorkshire, northern England	July 2002 (R)	Stokenchurch, Oxfordshire: March 2003	250km SSE	Made at least two visits to the Chilterns in spring 2003, returning to Yorkshire on each occasion after 17 and 11 days respectively
Suffolk, eastern England	July 1997 (F)	The Netherlands: November 1998	c.150km E	Previously recorded at feeding site in Wales. The other two young from this nest also dispersed, one to Wales, the other to southern England
Wales	July 1970 (F)	Wrotham, near Maidstone, Kent: August 1970	315km ESE	Found dead on railway line. A small proportion of Welsh young disperse into England each year
Wales	June 1992 (F)	Gas rig off north Norfolk coast: 19 July 1992	390km ENE	A surprisingly early date for such a long distance movement by a recently fledged bird

Table 16: (*Continued*)

Area of origin	Release (R) or fledging (F) date	Location and date recorded	Distance/direction travelled	Comments
Wales	July 1995 (F)	Ballyvaldon, Wexford, Ireland: October 1999	c.200km W	Found dead. The first overseas recovery of a Welsh ringed Red Kite
Central Scotland	July 2003 (F)	Airao, near Porto, Portugal: November 2003	c.2,000km SSW	Found with injured wing. Longest movement so far recorded for British Red Kite. Released in Portugal following rehabilitation. This is the second Scottish bird to be recorded in Iberia, another being found near Bilbao, northern Spain in 1999
Central Scotland	July 1997 (R)	Elkstone, Gloucestershire: February 1998	506km SSE	Had returned to the release area by mid-May 1998
Northern Scotland	July 1995 (F)	Stokenchurch, Oxfordshire: January and March 1996	720km SSE	Seen at southern England communal roost. Also recorded at roost in Yorkshire and central England before returning to its natal area to breed
Northern Scotland	July 1997 (F)	Cape Clear Island, Co. Cork, Ireland: October 1997	820km SW	An estimated 10% of Scottish Red Kites move to Ireland in their first autumn
Northern Scotland	July 1997 (F)	Iceland: December 1997-November 1999	1,020km NW	See text for further details
Northern Scotland	July 2000 (F)	Devon, southwest England: December 2000-January 2001	730km S	An unusual winter movement. Sightings show this bird moved south in November or December 2000, then back north to the natal area in late January 2001

Table 17: **Dispersal of released Red Kites in southern England, central England and northern Scotland in their first year**
(from Carter et al. 2003)

Year of release programme	Proportion of birds dispersing>50km (sample size)[1]			Territorial pairs in local population		
	Southern England	Central England[2]	Northern Scotland	Southern England	Central England	Northern Scotland
1	100 (5)	60 (10)	100 (6)	0	0	0
2	38 (13)	37 (16)	79 (19)	0	1	0
3	40 (15)	40 (20)	60 (20)	2	5	0
4	35 (20)	15 (20)	38 (24)	7	8	2
5	35 (20)	–	25 (24)	12	–	8

[1] Figures for dispersing birds are minimum values as some short-term movements away from the release areas will go undetected

[2] Figures for central England are for birds dispersing in their first autumn only

expected from these examples of long distance movements, Red Kites fledged elsewhere in Europe are often recorded in Britain, either as passage migrants or, less often, as permanent recruits (see Chapter 4 for more details).

In the re-establishing populations in Britain, the proportion of youngsters that undertake dispersive movements tends to decrease as population size increases (Evans *et al.* 1999, Carter *et al.* 2003 – see Table 17). For example, in the first year of releases, all of the birds released in southern England and northern Scotland made movements of more than 50km in their first year. By the final year of releases, with a small breeding population established in both areas, only 35% and 25% of released birds were recorded more than 50km from the release areas in southern England and northern Scotland respectively. This trend reflects the inherently social nature of the Red Kite, with the release area becoming a more attractive proposition for young birds once it supports a small population as a result of previous releases.

For reasons that are not fully understood, the proportion of birds moving away from the release areas has been higher in Scotland than in England and this is one of the reasons that population growth has been more rapid in England. Although there is a tendency for birds to return to their release area following dispersal, they become more vulnerable to persecution once they move away from the area where landowners are familiar with them, and survival rates are therefore lower. It is unlikely that a greater proportion of Scottish Red Kites disperse due to differences in food supply as survival rates for birds that remain close to the release sites are as high as they are in England and there appears to be no shortage of food in any of the release areas. This is particularly true in the early stages of a project when intraspecific competition is low as a result of the small number of Red Kites in the area. It is also unclear why, when a group of birds are released together at the same site, some 'choose' to disperse whilst others remain in the release area. It is likely that the tendency to disperse is at least partly governed by the genetic make-up of individuals. If this is the case then the fact that birds released in Scotland were taken from largely migratory populations in Sweden and Germany, whereas those released in England came mostly from resident populations in Spain, may help to explain the difference. The fact that two young Scottish Red Kites have now been found in Iberia (see Table 16) where many birds from Sweden and Germany spend the winter is perhaps instructive.

Very few adult birds in resident populations undertake long-distance movements between breeding sites once they have bred for the first time, although such behaviour is occasionally recorded following a breeding failure. This is a sensible strategy and one that is followed by many long-lived birds as, by remaining in the same area, individuals benefit from the knowledge they have built up of their surroundings. Their chances of surviving a period of poor weather or of rearing chicks successfully are improved by knowing, through experience, where food and shelter are most likely to be found. This is shown well by records of wing-tagged adult birds in Wales found breeding at different sites. A total of 85 birds were found to have moved more than 2km between breeding sites used in different years but, of these, only eight moved more than 6km. The longest recorded movement between breeding sites over many years of observations was 30.5km (Davis *et al*. 2001).

Natal philopatry and range expansion

Young Red Kites show a strong tendency to breed for the first time close to the site where they themselves were reared. This applies even to individuals that disperse away from their birthplace, as many subsequently return to the natal area before they reach breeding age. Faithfulness to the natal site is demonstrated well by the large number of Welsh birds that have been marked as chicks and subsequently found breeding. Of 139 birds whose breeding site was subsequently located, the average distance moved from birthplace to breeding site was 12.5km (Cross & Davis 1998). The mean distance between natal site and site of first breeding for nine radio-tagged birds in the high-density southern England population was only 3km (Dixon 2001). A larger sample of southern

Figure 9: **Records of Red Kites in central England that dispersed more than 20km away from their release site, 1995-98**

■ Release site

England birds identifiable from their wing-tags were found to have established breeding sites an average of 4km from their natal site with a maximum distance of 17km and a minimum distance of only 0.25km (Snell *et al*. 2002).

In southern England, Red Kites have been slow to recolonise vacant habitat even though breeding productivity within the highest density parts of the range has declined (Snell *et al*. 2002), probably due to increasing competition for food between breeding adults. As densities increase further, productivity may continue to fall and age of first breeding may rise as it becomes more difficult for young adults to find an unoccupied nesting site or sufficient food to reach breeding condition. From a human perspective it seems nonsensical that young adults in this situation do not simply move to ideal, but currently unoccupied, habitat where there is no competition for food or shortage of nest sites. However, by returning to the area where it was reared successfully, a young Red Kite is selecting an area that it knows with certainty provided suitable habitat. Without actually making a breeding attempt there may be no reliable means of assessing the suitability of other areas, particularly areas where other Red Kites are not present, and an individual risks wasting valuable resources if it decides to take a chance. Natal philopatry evolved long before human persecution became a significant factor, when the most likely reason for an area being devoid of Red Kites was that it did not provide suitable habitat. Before human persecution wiped out Red Kites from many areas of high quality habitat, an inbuilt tendency to avoid areas where Red Kites were not already present would have been a sensible strategy.

There are exceptions to the general pattern of faithfulness to the natal site and a few of the more adventurous birds do end up breeding well away from their own birthplace. Usually such movements are from one Red Kite population to another and there are several examples of birds from the reintroduced populations in England and Scotland that have bred away from the population where they were reared or released. A bird fledged in northern Scotland has bred in central Scotland and there has been recruitment in both directions between the central and southern England populations, only about 100km apart. A bird from Yorkshire made an unsuccessful breeding attempt in central Scotland, about 300km to the north, in 2004. The only bird from one of the reintroduced populations that has so far been recorded breeding in Wales was a female released in central England in 1997 and found dead on a Welsh nest in spring 2000. There are no proven examples of Welsh birds breeding in England or Scotland although, as many Welsh young are not fitted with wing-tags, such movements could easily have taken place without being detected. Genetic studies have shown that Red Kites fledged elsewhere in Europe have, at least on rare occasions, recruited into breeding populations in Britain. Analysis of DNA in blood samples has shown that genetic traits found in central European Red Kites are now present in both the Welsh and southern English populations (May *et al.* 1993a; Ian Evans pers. comm.).

It is much more unusual for Red Kites that move away from their birthplace to end up breeding away from other established populations. This may be partly due to lack of opportunity, as a bird settled in unoccupied habitat is unlikely to meet up with a bird of the opposite sex, and partly for the reasons discussed above, relating to the social nature of the species. Occasionally, however, breeding pairs do become established in a new area. In eastern England an isolated pair bred in northeast Suffolk for two consecutive years in 1996 and 1997, rearing a total of five young. Based on the breeding date it was thought most likely that the adults were migrants from the continent (Carter 1998). There were hopes that a small population might become established but the pair did not breed again in 1998 and all the young from the previous two years dispersed away from the nest site (see Table 16). If these young survived into adulthood then it seems that the instinct to breed in an area already supporting a well-established Red Kite population may have proved stronger than the instinct to return to breed at the natal site.

In the last few years several other isolated pairs, involving birds from the reintroduction programme, have bred in England. The extent to which such adventurous pairs are able to found new populations well away from the release areas will have a major impact on the speed at which the Red Kite recolonises vacant habitat in Britain. Population expansion up until now has been mainly through a gradual spread out from the main core of breeding birds in each of the release areas.

Differences between the sexes

All young birds released in England and Scotland have been sexed from the DNA in blood samples. As a result of monitoring their movements following release, differences in dispersal behaviour between the sexes have become apparent. Evans *et al*. (1999) analysed the movements of 73 birds released in southern England and 92 birds released in northern Scotland. In England, 29% of males and 53% of females moved more than 50km away from the release site in their first year, while in Scotland, the equivalent figures were 42% for males and 57.5% for females. In central England there was a similar disparity between the sexes leading to an eventual excess of males in the population despite the fact that more females than males were released (Carter & Grice 2000). The difference in dispersal behaviour between the sexes is also clearly apparent from movements of Welsh birds although there is a limited sample size due to the difficulty in sexing birds. Of 15 birds that made long-distance movements and were recorded outside Wales in 1987-93, the sex of 11 was known, all of which were females. In fact, there is only one example of a known male having emigrated from Wales and that was found in the adjacent county of Herefordshire having travelled 60km from its natal site (Davis *et al*. 2001).

In most species where there is a greater tendency for females to disperse, it is the males that are responsible for establishing breeding territories in order to attract a female (Campbell & Lack 1985) and this does appear to be the case with the Red Kite. In this situation, males may increase their chances of successfully establishing a territory and attracting a female if they spend more time in one area, becoming as familiar as possible with the locality and its most productive foraging areas. Females are less constrained and so are more likely to explore further afield, perhaps on the lookout for alternative breeding opportunities in other areas.

Adult females tend to utilise smaller home ranges than males during the breeding season which is not surprising given the male bird's greater responsibility for food provisioning. To find that such a difference is maintained during the winter is unexpected, but there is some evidence for this from an intensive radio-tracking study in southern Spain (Heredia *et al*. 1991). Although the study was based on a sample of only two males and three females it found that males ranged further from their winter roost sites and utilised significantly larger home ranges than females. A radio-tracking study in Germany provides support for this finding although it was based on only a single pair of Red Kites. During the winter of 1998/99 the female of the pair roosted away from the breeding site on only 11 nights, 7% of the total. In contrast, the male bird spent 18% of nights away from its breeding site (Nachtigall *et al*. 2003). Heredia *et al*. (1991) suggested that, by not ranging as widely as males during the winter, females were better able to build up reserves for the forthcoming breeding season. This could be very important as, during incubation and the early chick period, females are restricted to the nest site and must rely mainly on food that the male is able to provide. It is also possible that, being confined to the nest and its immediate vicinity for a substantial part of the breeding season, the female does not develop as large a home range as the male, choosing instead to rely on the small area with which she is most familiar, throughout the year.

7. *Adult Red Kite snatching up road-kill in Germany. This is just one of the food sources unwittingly provided by humans that the Red Kite is readily able to exploit*   *(Robert Groß)*

8. *Red Kites are capable of flying at considerable speed but slow circling or leisurely drifting over the countryside, as with this juvenile, is more typical*   *(Chris Gomersall)*

9. *Chicks only a few days old covered with thick down - pure white on the head but darker and with a sandy tint on the body and wings* *(Tony Cross)*

10. *When chicks are about 7-10 days old they are still covered with down and the first true feathers are only just beginning to develop* *(Ian Carter)*

11. *Chick about 2-2.5 weeks old with adult at the nest. The emerging feathers are now clearly visible on the body and wings, and the tail is just starting to grow* (Mike Read)

12. *Chick about five weeks old. By this stage, the body and wings are covered in brown feathers and only traces of down remain on a few feather tips and on the head* (Mike Read)

13. *This poisoning incident, involving a Brown Hare carcass laced with mevinphos, resulted in the death of at least three young Red Kites in Northamptonshire* *(Ian Carter)*

14. *Corvids, in this case a Carrion Crow, are a frequent source of irritation to the Red Kite due to their aggressive mobbing behaviour* *(Chris Gomersall)*

Chapter 11

MORTALITY AND SURVIVAL

The Red Kite's frequent association with human settlements, its slow, often low, languid flight, and its preference for animal carrion, all make it highly vulnerable to human persecution and accidental secondary poisoning resulting from pest control campaigns. Poisoning, in particular, is a major problem and no other European bird of prey is as vulnerable to this threat as the Red Kite. Indeed, deliberate and accidental poisoning are the main reasons for the bird's highly patchy distribution in Europe. In areas where it is left unmolested, Red Kite numbers are often high but, where poisons are used carelessly or in baits intended to kill predators and scavengers, the species may be rare or absent, despite the availability of suitable habitat. The Red Kite has few natural enemies when full-grown, but adults are occasionally killed by other large birds of prey and, as with any wild bird, there are some losses as a result of disease and starvation.

Human persecution

Illegal persecution, in several different forms, is still the main threat to the Red Kite across much of its range. The Red Kite is not always the main target of persecution and this is particularly the case with poison baits placed out in the open countryside. These are usually aimed at predators such as Foxes or corvids but are completely indiscriminate and the Red Kite's supreme ability to detect animal carrion means that it is often first on the scene and so suffers disproportionately. In some areas, despite its mainly scavenging lifestyle, the Red Kite itself is viewed as a threat to game species or poultry, and here, direct persecution, including nest destruction, trapping and shooting, is an additional threat.

With increased legal protection and changing public attitudes towards birds of prey, levels of persecution in central and northern Europe have greatly reduced over recent decades. This has led to the recovery of populations that were drastically reduced by human activities in the past. The Red Kite reintroduction programme in Britain was only possible following a reduction in persecution, although illegal killing is still far too frequent and has slowed the rate of population increase and spread to new areas, particularly in Scotland. In southern and eastern Europe, persecution remains as one of the most important factors affecting Red Kites and populations will only recover if this problem can be tackled effectively.

Even in areas where Red Kites are studied intensively, only a small proportion of dead birds are ever likely to be recovered so that the cause of death can be established. In the reintroduced populations in England, it has been estimated, based on survival rates determined for individually-marked birds, that only about one in five birds that die is recovered for post-mortem (Holmes *et al.* 2000, 2003). The others are either found when badly decomposed so that the cause of death can not be determined or are not found at all. In populations where there is no wing-tagging and radio-tracking, the proportion of birds found will be far lower. Where illegal killing is involved, it is clearly in the interests of those involved to conceal the evidence of their activities where possible. For these reasons, it should be stressed that the figures given below, referring to birds killed by humans, represent only the tip of the iceberg.

Illegal poisoning

This has been the major threat faced by the Red Kite during the last 150 years or more and one of the main factors that led to the complete loss of the species from parts of its range, including England and Scotland. It is a method of control that was once widely used by farmers and gamekeepers because it provided a cheap and easy method for destroying a whole range of predatory species. Baits, either animal carcasses or eggs, laced with poison and placed out in the open can account for a number of individuals with a minimum of effort, whereas shooting and trapping are far more time consuming and often less effective. Since becoming illegal in Britain, the use of poison baits has declined and legitimate pest species are now more often controlled by legal means such as shooting, snaring and through setting cage traps. Unfortunately, a minority of individuals in Britain continue to use poison baits, ignoring both the legislation and the weight of public opinion firmly against this illegal and outdated activity. Birds of prey continue to be regular victims.

The Red Kite is especially vulnerable to poisoning because it is such an efficient, opportunist scavenger and often gathers in numbers at a source of food. As a result, many individuals may be killed by a single bait. The recovery of the Welsh population has long been hindered by the use of poison baits to control Foxes and corvids, blamed by farmers for killing lambs. Between 1950 and 1999, a total of 38 Welsh Red Kites were found poisoned including five birds in one incident in 1989 (Lovegrove 1990, Davis *et al*. 2001). In 1999, a single incident resulted in the death of only one Red Kite but also at least one Buzzard, several Carrion Crows and no fewer than 19 Ravens, clearly demonstrating the indiscriminate effects of poison baits. An analysis of 155 Welsh Red Kites found dead between 1950 and 1999 revealed that 25% were definitely poisoned and a further 12% were probably poisoned, together representing 57% of the birds for which it was possible to establish a likely cause of death (Davis *et al*. 2001).

The reintroduced populations have also suffered from illegal poisoning and this is by far the most frequent cause of death for Red Kites in England and Scotland. In the period from 1989 to 2000, 20 birds were found dead as a result of illegal poisoning in England and a further bird was poisoned but recovered and was released back into the wild (Carter & Grice 2000, Holmes *et al*. 2003). As only about one in five dead birds are recovered (see above), this suggests that around 100 birds were killed by poison baits in this short period, despite the small size of the reintroduced populations. The problem is even greater in Scotland where, between 1997 and 2000 alone, at least 13 Red Kites were found illegally poisoned. Statistical analysis of the cause of death of 248 young

Red Kites in northern Scotland between 1999 and 2003 (based on a sample of birds found dead) suggested that no fewer than 114 birds (46% of the total) had been killed by poisoning (Brian Etheridge pers. comm.). This problem is especially associated with moorland areas managed by gamekeepers for Red Grouse shooting (Whitfield *et al.* 2003) and Red Kites wandering to such areas often fail to return. This is the main reason for the dramatic difference between the success of the reintroduced populations on the Black Isle in northern Scotland and the Chilterns in southern England, despite the release of the same number of birds in each area. The Black Isle population has stalled at 35-40 breeding pairs, with few young surviving until they are old enough to breed, whereas the Chilterns population has increased to well over 300 pairs in the same period. The late Donald Dewer, when Secretary of State for Scotland, made his feelings clear when he referred to the continued high levels of persecution of birds of prey in Scotland as 'a national disgrace', a sentiment shared by all who enjoy watching these spectacular birds.

There is an ongoing Government-led campaign to reduce illegal poisoning in Britain and the Red Kite has certainly played a useful role in helping to raise public awareness of this issue and the seriousness with which it is viewed by the authorities. In 1997, for example, a farmer in southern England was prosecuted and fined £4,000 for deliberately poisoning a Red Kite. The case received considerable local publicity and has hopefully deterred others from carrying out similar activities in the area. There have been encouraging signs, in England at least, of a reduction in poisoning incidents involving Red Kites in recent years.

In Spain, Villafuerte *et al.* (1998) found a strong correlation between areas with important populations of Rabbits (a valued game species in Spain) and recent declines in Red Kite numbers, and attributed this to persecution, particularly poisoning. Many hunters in Spain view large birds of prey as a threat to Rabbit populations and some still resort to using illegal methods to control their numbers. In parts of Spain, baits are still put out in order to try to kill Wolves and other mammalian predators blamed for taking livestock or gamebirds, and this adds to the risk that birds of prey will be poisoned. Only in areas where game shooting is not important are Red Kite populations stable or increasing. The situation is thought to have worsened following a recent reduction in Rabbit numbers as a result of viral haemorrhagic disease. Some hunters have wrongly blamed the decline on predators and, as a result, persecution has increased. A similar situation existed in Spain in the 1950s, when myxomatosis was responsible for a substantial reduction in the Rabbit population. During this period there was a Government-sponsored campaign targeted at predators in order to try to maintain Rabbit numbers and it was estimated that as many as 10,000 Red and Black Kites were killed between 1954 and 1961 (Garzón 1974).

It is impossible to know how many Red Kites have been killed in more recent times in Spain as controlling birds of prey is now illegal and incidents are therefore not widely reported. However, no fewer than 408 Red Kites were found poisoned between 1990 and 2000, second only to Griffon Vulture in terms of numbers, clearly demonstrating the scale of the problem (Mañosa 2002, Viñuela & Villafuerte 2003). In an earlier review, Hernández (1997) concluded that the Red Kite was the species worst affected by this problem in Spain and gave summary details of 150 birds poisoned in only 16 incidents. Worryingly, 17 wintering birds found poisoned in northern Spain had been ringed as nestlings in Germany (Viñuela & Villafuerte 2003), showing the potential for this threat to affect breeding populations in other areas, as well as the local population.

Poisoning also affects Red Kites in parts of Europe where populations are still very low and the loss of even a small number of individuals is of great concern. In The Netherlands, for example, where breeding is only occasionally recorded, 12 Red Kites were poisoned between 1976 and 1980, no doubt reducing the prospects for recolonisation (Cadbury 1991).

In many areas, the use of poison baits is more intensive in spring and summer as this is when lambs and young gamebirds are most vulnerable to predators. In Wales, for example, 66% of Red Kite deaths from poisoning occurred between February and May (Davis *et al.* 2001). In Spain, 70% of poisoning cases involving birds of prey are in the spring months (Viñuela & Villafuerte 2003). This adds to the impact of the problem as Red Kites are breeding at this time of year. The loss of adult birds in spring breaks up established breeding pairs and reduces the number of young reared, as well as reducing the number of adult birds in the population.

The type of poison favoured for use in baits varies from area to area depending on what is most readily available. The following list gives details of the most frequently abused poisons in Britain:

Fenthion: A discontinued organophosphorus veterinary product formerly used by farmers to control warble fly infestations in sheep and therefore widely available. This is the most commonly used illegal poison in Wales and has presumably been stockpiled by some for this purpose.

Mevinphos: A highly toxic organophosphorus insecticide formerly available under the trade name 'Phosdrin' but no longer approved for agricultural use. It has been stockpiled by some people for use in poison baits, and, until recently, was the poison most commonly involved in Red Kite incidents in England.

Strychnine: Licensed for use underground to control Moles but also highly toxic to birds and frequently used illegally in poison baits.

Alphachloralose: A narcotic used as a bird stupefying agent and a rodenticide. The high concentration formula used in illegal baits is only available under licence to pest controllers, although there is some evidence that it is also imported illegally from sources in the Republic of Ireland (RSPB Investigations Unit). Until recently, this was the pesticide most frequently used for poisoning wildlife in Britain.

Carbofuran: A highly-toxic carbamate insecticide formerly used on root crops, brassicas and cereals but no longer legally available. The first recorded persecution incident was in 1988 but, in Scotland, it is now the pesticide most frequently recorded in wildlife poisoning incidents.

Various other compounds, mainly agricultural pesticides, have been responsible for the death of Red Kites when used in poison baits. These include metaldehyde (found in slug pellets), diazinon, malathion, aldicarb, endrin and phorate. In Spain, carbofuran and fenthion have been responsible for the majority of Red Kite poisoning incidents.

Shooting

It is very difficult to assess the true impact of illegal shooting on Red Kite populations as birds shot and killed, or injured badly enough to be captured, will inevitably be concealed by the perpetrator. Only when the act of shooting is witnessed or if a bird is injured and later found and reported, do incidents come to light. As in the case of poisoning, the Red Kite is particularly vulnerable to this form of persecution as its nest and roost sites are easy to find and it often flies slowly, low over the ground, in search of food, presenting a relatively easy target. Added to this, it often forages around human settlements, offering more frequent opportunities for shooting than is the case with other, more elusive, birds of prey.

In England, since the start of the reintroduction programme, at least four birds have been found with shotgun injuries. Three were successfully rehabilitated by vets at the Institute of Zoology, based at London Zoo, and released back into the wild. The fourth failed to respond sufficiently well to treatment and had to be destroyed. In addition, a number of birds found dead have been shown to contain lead from shotgun cartridges when x-rayed. One bird found dead on a railway line in the Chilterns, presumably killed by a train, was found to have two different sizes of lead shot in its body, indicating that it had been shot and wounded on two separate occasions (Carter & Grice 2002). The Scottish population has also suffered from this problem with post-mortems suggesting that as many as 8% of young birds in northern Scotland between 1999 and 2003 were killed in this way (Brian Etheridge pers. comm.).

Shooting is thought to be a significant problem in parts of Spain. In 1992-94, 25 cases of shooting were witnessed during 500 visits made to 268 communal roost sites (Viñuela & Villafuerte 2003). By assuming that one bird was killed for each shooting event (probably conservative for shooting at communal roosts) and extrapolating this rate of shooting to the overall wintering population, the authors estimated that several thousand birds may be shot in Spain each winter, comprising both resident Spanish Red Kites and wintering central European birds. In other southern European countries with large numbers of hunters but mainly low numbers of Red Kites, opportunist shooting is also likely to occur, although good information is lacking.

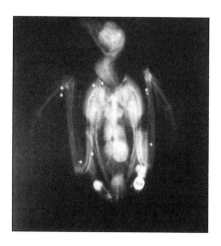

The numerous lead pellets from a shotgun cartridge are clearly visible in this x-ray of a wounded Red Kite in England (Institute of Zoology)

Egg collecting

Ever since British Red Kites were reduced to a small remnant population in mid-Wales in the early 1900s, their eggs have been highly sought after by collectors, and this is one of the factors that has prevented a more rapid recovery of the Welsh population. In the 1950s and 1960s when the number of known

201

nests was between ten and 24, very few years went by without at least one nest being robbed and many incidents no doubt went undetected. In 1956, only three young were known to have fledged and yet at least four nests were robbed of their eggs, severely reducing breeding productivity in that year. In 1985, no fewer than ten nests were robbed, affecting over one fifth of the total breeding population (Lovegrove 1990), and in most years during the 1990s, clutches were taken.

Strenuous efforts have been made to protect nests from egg collectors, involving the use of sophisticated electronic equipment, as well as the more labour-intensive 24-hour protection watches. Even the army has been drafted in to watch over nests thought to be particularly at risk. In some cases, where nests were known to be vulnerable, the decision was taken to remove the eggs so that they could be hatched and reared safely in captivity (Lovegrove *et al*. 1990), the adult birds sometimes being given Buzzard eggs to incubate so that they continued to sit. The artificially reared young from the rescued eggs were then placed in a suitable foster nest when about ten days old. The adult Red Kites readily accept this unlikely sequence of events, with eggs suddenly being replaced by well-grown chicks or an extra chick appearing in the nest. This nest manipulation programme has resulted in over 50 young, reared from eggs taken into captivity, being returned to nests in the wild (Tony Cross pers. comm.). As the Welsh population continues to increase, so the impact of a few lost clutches each year diminishes. Nevertheless, each nest that fails as a result of human interference inevitably slows the rate of population increase and spread to new areas.

The reintroduced populations have been affected relatively little by egg collecting, perhaps because collectors prefer to target the native population in Wales and also because, as Red Kite numbers have increased, there has been a corresponding reduction in the 'rarity value' of the eggs. Nevertheless, there is evidence that several clutches have been stolen from nests in southern England. Following a recent strengthening of the legislation, those taking the eggs of protected birds in Britain now face the prospect of a jail sentence. Several convicted collectors have been jailed in recent years and there are signs that this is beginning to have a deterrent effect, with a reduction in recorded incidents. Although some eggs will no doubt continue to be taken as Red Kites spread into new areas, it is hoped that the impact of this outdated activity will be minimal in future.

Accidental secondary poisoning

Incidents where birds of prey are poisoned accidentally as a consequence of the legal use, or accidental misuse, of a pesticide are of great concern as they are particularly difficult to prevent. The most dramatic example of this form of poisoning involved the elimination of the Peregrine and Sparrowhawk from large parts of their range in Britain, and elsewhere, following the widespread use of organochlorine pesticides such as DDT, endrin and dieldrin (Newton 1979). These were used as insecticides in the 1950s and 1960s, often being added as a seed-dressing to cereal grain before sowing. Although they have a relatively low direct toxicity when compared to some other agricultural pesticides, they are extremely persistent in the environment and become concentrated in the bodies of predators at the top of the food chain. Despite the delaying tactics, and the hiding of unpalatable information, by pesticide manufacturers and others with vested interests, the case against these chemicals eventually became overwhelming and they were either banned or severely restricted in use, to be replaced by less persistent products (Ratcliffe 1993).

Hopefully, lessons have been learnt from this episode and, in Britain, there are now Government-run monitoring schemes in place, such as the Wildlife Incident Investigation Scheme (WIIS), in order to help identify potential problems with pesticides at an early stage. Post-mortems are carried out on dead mammals and birds reported to the scheme and, where poisoning is suspected, tissues are analysed for the presence of pesticides. The cause of death of many of the Red Kites referred to in the sections below was established as a result of dead birds being submitted to the WIIS scheme.

Agricultural pesticides

The widespread use of organochlorine pesticides throughout Europe in the 1950s and 1960s is thought to have had a serious impact on many raptor species in addition to the Sparrowhawk and Peregrine, although the studies required to confirm a link were often not carried out. Bijleveld (1974), for example, detailed a series of dramatic declines in birds of prey in Hungary between 1957 and 1967, including a 90% decline in the Red Kite, but could only speculate that the indiscriminate use of organochlorine pesticides was the main factor. However, studies did confirm that the eggs of many species, including the Red Kite, contained residues of organochlorines. In Germany, an average decrease in egg-shell thickness of 4.3% was found in Red Kite eggs collected in the 1950s, with the highest decrease in areas where intensive agriculture dominated the landscape (Weber & Stubbe 1995). Although of concern, this is a small decrease compared to the 20% reduction found in some species and may not have reduced breeding productivity significantly.

In the early 1960s, dieldrin, one of the organochlorines, was widely used in sheep-dips in Wales. Red Kite breeding productivity was particularly poor during this period and it is possible that, through scavenging on sheep carcasses, birds were being adversely affected by secondary poisoning. This was shown to be the case with the Golden Eagle in western Scotland (Lockie *et al*. 1969) but the evidence for a similar effect in Welsh Red Kites was not conclusive. Analysis of unhatched Red Kite eggs revealed only low levels of organochlorine residues and measurements of egg-shells showed a relatively low average reduction in thickness of 4.5% (Davis & Newton 1981). Dieldrin was withdrawn from use in sheep-dips in 1965, thus removing the potential for adverse effects on Red Kites. Other chemicals used in sheep-dips have also been implicated in the death of adult Red Kites including diazinon and propetamphos, which are still in use today. Poisoning can potentially result either from scavenging on sheep carcasses or the careless disposal of used dip, perhaps resulting in the contamination of earthworms in pasture (Davis *et al*. 2001). In Scotland, recent incidents involving the death of Red Kites are believed to have resulted from lambs with tail-docking rings being treated before their tails were lost. Dropped tails are often found in Red Kite nests, brought in either as food or as nest lining, and could result in poisoning if consumed following recent treatment with pesticide.

A small number of recent Red Kite poisoning incidents in Britain are thought to have involved the misuse of agricultural pesticides, resulting from a failure to follow the label instructions of a product, rather than a deliberate attempt to poison wildlife. An example of this type of incident is the spillage of pesticide-treated grain when it is approved for use only if drilled directly into the soil in order to make it inaccessible to birds. This may result in the death of grain feeders such as pigeons and, with highly toxic products, there is then a risk of secondary poisoning of predators or scavengers. In 2000 in central England, a four-week old Red Kite nestling was found dead on a nest, together with a partly consumed Woodpigeon containing pink-dyed maize seed. Analysis revealed the presence of bendiocarb, a seed dressing, in both the maize and tissues from the nestling, and it was concluded that the chick had been poisoned. It is likely that, through carelessness, some of the treated maize had been spilled onto the ground and so was accessible to the Woodpigeon. Another incident in England involved the misuse of the pesticide phorate which had been used to treat a field bean crop, but had not been incorporated into the soil as required by the label instructions. Although such incidents are only recorded occasionally, they are undoubtedly difficult to detect and continued vigilance is required to ensure that potentially dangerous agricultural pesticides are used correctly with minimal risks to wildlife. Where there is evidence that a pesticide has been misused, leading to the death of non-target wildlife species, those responsible risk prosecution and a substantial penalty.

Rodenticides

The Red Kite has helped to highlight a potentially serious problem with the highly toxic second-generation anticoagulant rodenticides that are now used widely across Europe. Although these products are sold under a bewildering variety of different trade names, they are all based on a small number of active ingredients, namely difenacoum, bromadiolone, brodifacoum and flocoumafen. They are effective in areas where Brown Rats have developed resistance to first generation poisons such as warfarin, and they can kill with only a single feed, whereas warfarin requires several feeds in order to be effective. The problem for wildlife stems from the fact that they are up to several hundred times more toxic than warfarin, and so there is a far greater risk of secondary poisoning when predators or scavengers feed on poisoned rodents. Second-generation rodenticides also have relatively long biological half-lives and are slow to break down once in the tissues of an animal. It is therefore possible for a damaging level of rodenticide to build up through the repeated ingestion of relatively small doses in poisoned prey.

Although problems with rodenticide poisoning have been reported for several species in Britain, most notably the Barn Owl (Newton *et al.* 1999) and Polecat (Shore *et al.* 1996), there are three aspects of the Red Kite's ecology that, taken together, make it particularly vulnerable to this threat (Carter & Burn 2000, Ntampakis & Carter 2005):

(i)   In some areas, Brown Rats form a major part of the diet throughout the year. They are an especially useful food in the breeding season as they provide a large meal but are usually light enough to be carried back to the nest

(ii) The Red Kite is a scavenger and most rodents are taken as carrion, where there is a greater chance of contamination by rodenticides

(iii) Red Kites frequently forage close to human settlements, including farm buildings, where rodent control is frequently carried out. Experimental work has shown that Red Kites will take dead rodents placed close to farm buildings, often within a single day

This problem first came to light in reintroduced Red Kites in 1998 and 1999 when tissue samples from eight dead birds in England were found to contain residues of second-generation rodenticides. Post-mortems carried out on three of these birds revealed internal bleeding, strongly suggesting that the anticoagulant effect of the poison was the cause of death. Then, in 1999 and 2000, six nestlings from three different nests in northern Scotland were found dead on, or close to, the nest. Residues of bromadiolone or difenacoum were found in the liver of each bird and post-mortems again revealed internal bleeding, showing that they had been poisoned (Brian Etheridge in litt.).

Recent studies carried out by the Centre for Ecology and Hydrology (at Monks Wood) and the Scottish Agricultural Science Agency found that 65% of 29 liver samples, from birds that had died from a variety of different causes in England and Scotland, contained rodenticide residues, although not all at levels thought likely to have caused death (Sharp & Hunter 1999, Shore et al. 2000). This is a far higher proportion than seen in Barn Owls, for example, where the figure is about 35% for dead birds tested in recent years (Newton et al. 1999). Such a widespread level of contamination is of great concern, particularly as the residues were often above the levels found in Barn Owls known to have died as a result of rodenticide poisoning. There have been relatively few incidents of rodenticide poisoning involving Red Kites in Wales where the mainly pastoral landscape is less well suited to Brown Rats and they are not common in the diet (Davis & Davis 1981).

On the continent, second-generation rodenticides are used to reduce agricultural damage caused by vole plagues and this has led to mass mortalities of birds of prey as a result of secondary poisoning. In Switzerland, for example, an incident in the early 1980s involving the use of bromadiolone to control Water Voles (an agricultural pest in parts of Europe!) led to the death of no fewer than 25 Red Kites as well as other raptor species (Beguin 1983). More recently, the use of bromadiolone to control voles has led to the death of many Red Kites in France and Spain. This problem has been implicated in local declines in the breeding population in parts of France, and has the potential to affect birds from central Europe wintering in Spain (Ligue pour la Protection des Oiseaux in litt., Viñuela et al. 1999).

In Britain, the problem shows no signs of improving as Brown Rats have benefited from a lack of severe winters in recent years and, in a few areas, have even started to develop resistance to some of the second-generation poisons. Although there are strict controls on the way that rodenticides can be used, such as the requirement for bait to be placed within a secure container, it is difficult to prevent some animals dying out in the open where they are accessible to scavengers. This is the case even with the most toxic products containing brodifacoum or flocoumafen, which are only authorised for use inside buildings.

The use of vitamin K in animal feeds is a further cause for concern as this acts as an antidote to anticoagulant rodenticides. Rodents that gain access to such feeds may require a higher dose of poison to kill them, presenting a greater risk of secondary poisoning.

This is a very difficult issue to resolve. There is clearly a need to control Brown Rats in Britain and vole plagues on the continent where they are causing problems, and the use of anticoagulant rodenticides is usually the most effective method. In many areas, the less toxic first-generation rodenticides such as warfarin are still effective and they should be used in preference to second-generation products because they carry a lower risk of secondary poisoning. Alternative forms of control, such as trapping, may also be effective in some situations. Where second-generation rodenticides must be used, it is essential that frequent searches for rodent carcasses are carried out, as required by the product label instructions, and any carcasses found must be disposed of safely by burning or burying, rather than thrown onto an open dump where they are accessible to scavengers. Failure to make regular searches for dead rodents, or the use of rodenticides contrary to any of the other legally-binding label instructions can lead to prosecution and a heavy fine.

Lead poisoning

Birds become vulnerable to lead poisoning, either by ingesting lead directly, as in the well-known example of the Mute Swan and lead fishing weights, or by feeding on prey species killed or injured by lead ammunition. Although lead ingested by a bird of prey is subsequently regurgitated, along with other indigestible material from prey, during the time it is in the acidic stomach it gradually dissolves, releasing the highly toxic lead into the bloodstream (Pain et al. 1995). In some circumstances, a single lead-shot may be sufficient to cause death but even where only a small amount of lead enters the bloodstream, repeated ingestion of contaminated prey can result in lead levels building up to a high enough level to have an adverse effect. Marsh Harriers in southern France, for example, have been lethally poisoned by feeding on shot wildfowl, including scavenging on birds killed outright and taking live prey containing lead-shot as a result of a non-lethal injury (Pain et al. 1993).

Analysis of regurgitated Red Kite pellets in England and Scotland has shown that lead from shotgun cartridges is, at times, ingested, although it occurs in only a low proportion of pellets (Wildman et al. 1998, Pain et al. 2007). Lead-shot has also been found in Red Kite pellets in southern Spain, although the proportion containing lead was much lower than for Marsh Harriers and it was concluded that lead poisoning was unlikely to be a serious problem (Viñuela *et al*. 1999). In Britain, the most likely source of lead is through scavenging on gamebirds or pest species such as Woodpigeons or Rabbits, killed by shotgun. All these species are common in the Red Kite's diet and so there is a risk that sufficient lead could be ingested to result in poisoning. Wildfowl might also present a problem. Although recent legislation has outlawed the used of lead for killing waterbirds, recent research has shown that a high proportion of wild ducks bought for human consumption in England still contained lead-shot, despite the ban (Cromie *et al*. 2002).

Lead in rifle-shot animals can also result in poisoning, as fragments of lead bullet may remain lodged in the flesh to be swallowed by scavengers. This was one of the main factors that caused the endangered California Condor to decline and is now hindering efforts to reintroduce it (Meretsky *et al*. 1999). Farmers and gamekeepers in Britain control Rabbits by shooting them with a rifle, often at night when they are illuminated with high-powered lamps. The carcasses are frequently left where they fall, either because they are thought to reduce the likelihood of Fox predation of livestock or gamebirds, or simply because they have little value and it is time consuming to retrieve them. On some farms they are left specifically as food for the local Red Kites, unwittingly presenting a risk to the very birds they are intended to benefit.

Despite the threat posed by lead, there have been relatively few confirmed cases of poisoning. One involved a nestling collected in southern England in 2000 and taken to the Yorkshire release site. During its time in captivity it failed to develop at the same rate as the other birds in the pens and so was taken to the Institute of Zoology for veterinary assessment. Analysis of a blood sample showed that lead levels were very high and, despite treatment, lead poisoning eventually resulted in death (Andrew Cunningham pers. comm.). To help determine the true extent of this problem, samples of liver tissue from 20 Red Kites found dead in England between 1994 and 1999 were analysed for lead by the Centre for Ecology and Hydrology (Shore *et al*. 2000). Eleven of the 20 birds were found to have detectable lead residues, but only one bird had a residue noticeably higher than the usual background levels. However, a more recent study, based on a far larger sample of English birds, found that 39% had heightened lead levels with 8% having levels that were 'potentially toxic' to the birds and may have caused death (Eden 2002, Pain *et al*. 2007). The only way to completely remove this threat to Red Kites and other predators is to require the use of alternatives to lead in ammunition for all forms of shooting, extending the current restrictions that apply only to waterbirds. In order to avoid the problem for birds held in captivity as part of the reintroduction programme, only animals that have not been killed by shotgun are provided as food.

Electrocution and collision with powerlines

Mortality associated with powerlines has been reported for a wide range of species in various parts of the world. As a general rule, it is the heavier species with a high wing-loading, and therefore lower manoeuvrability, such as wildfowl and bustards, that are most vulnerable to collisions, whereas species with a large wing-span that habitually perch on the wire-supporting poles are at greater risk of electrocution (Janss 2000). Wing-span is important because, for a bird to be electrocuted, it must simultaneously touch either two separate wires or a wire and an earthed metal cross-support or transformer box, as it attempts to perch. If only a single wire is touched then the electricity does not pass through the body of the bird and many species habitually perch on live wires with no ill effects.

The Red Kite, with its generally leisurely flight and superb eyesight, but large wing-span and long tail, is more at risk from electrocution than collision (although see below) and this is borne out by a study of bird mortality associated with powerlines in southwest Spain (Janss 2000). The study involved walking or driving under lengths of powerline and recording the numbers of birds found dead from electrocution and collision. Electrocuted birds could be identified as they were mainly found under wires close to electricity poles and showed burn marks to the wings, talons or beak. Two different study areas were used, one containing powerlines thought to pose a high risk of collisions and the other with wires presenting a high risk of electrocution. Table 18 shows the number of individuals killed by electrocution and collision in each of the two areas, together with an index of local abundance for each species based on road transect counts. No Red or Black Kites were recorded as collision victims but both species were regular victims of electrocution. Nevertheless, the figures show that other species, in particular Buzzard and Raven, were far more vulnerable than the Red Kite to this threat, with many more individuals of each found electrocuted, despite their lower abundance in the study area. This is likely to be a reflection of their greater tendency to perch on telegraph poles than is the case with the two more aerial kite species.

Information from other studies of raptors around the world suggests that the threat from collision with powerlines has often been exaggerated in the past and many birds of prey reported as collision victims are now thought more likely to have been killed by electrocution (Bevanger & Overskaug 1998). This supports a reassessment of the threat posed by powerlines in Britain as it has previously been assumed by some authors that birds found dead below wires had been killed mainly by flying into them rather than by electrocution. There is now conclusive evidence that Red Kites are regularly electrocuted by the standard, three wire, electricity powerlines that are widespread across Britain. A minimum of

eight birds in Scotland (Brian Etheridge pers. comm.) and ten in England, have been killed in this way, all below wires adjacent to electricity poles, often with visible scorch marks on the wings or feet. Most of the birds were found close to poles with transformer boxes where the complex arrangement of wires, together with the fact that the transformer boxes are often earthed, makes electrocution more likely. One incident in central Scotland in spring 2006 emphasises just how serious this problem can be. Following up a report of a dead Red Kite, Duncan Cameron of the RSPB found the remains of no fewer than 43 dead birds beneath three adjacent power poles, including a Kestrel and a Buzzard in addition to the dead Red Kite. Most of the remaining birds were thought to be corvids although, in most cases, only the skull and bones remained.

There are various means of reducing the risk posed by powerlines. Coloured plastic balls or wire spirals may be attached to wires to make them more visible to birds. This has been done on powerlines close to important wetland reserves in Britain, such as the Ouse Washes in East Anglia, and has been successful in reducing the number of wildfowl killed by collision. Reducing the risk of electrocution is more difficult but can be done by insulating dangerous sections of wire, for exampe by covering them with a length of plastic tube, or, by providing artificial perches above the wires at dangerous poles. If Red Kites continue to fall victim to electrocution as populations expand in Britain then these types of solution will be worth serious consideration in order to limit the number of birds killed.

Collisions with vehicles and other structures

It is well-known that the Barn Owl suffers high mortality from collisions with vehicles in Britain (e.g. Shawyer 1998). Barn Owls hunt by quartering low over

Table 18: **Casualties of electrocution and collision found under powerlines in southwest Spain, 1991-93** *(from Janss 2000)*

Species	Deaths from electrocution	Local abundance index	Deaths from collision	Local abundance index
White Stork	36	648	5	42
Black Kite	46	631	0	26
Red Kite	45	446	0	61
Griffon Vulture	5	1060	1	283
Buzzard	167	195	0	37
Great Bustard	0	0	16	7
Little Bustard	0	0	10	0
Raven	117	38	0	42

the ground and birds may inadvertently fly into the path of an oncoming vehicle or, as a result of their lightweight bodies, get caught in the slipstream of high-sided vehicles, particularly when hunting over roadside verges. In the western United States, migrant Rough-legged Buzzards are regular victims of traffic. It is thought that their carrion-feeding habits attracts them to road-kills and their lack of familiarity with roads through breeding in remote parts of the arctic, makes them particularly vulnerable (Newton 1979). A relatively small number of Red Kites in Britain have been found dead or injured at the edge of a road with injuries consistent with having collided with passing traffic. Red Kites are normally very reluctant to land at carcasses, preferring to fly in ever-tighter circles before swooping down, grabbing the carcass, and carrying it away to a more secure feeding site. Larger carcasses are too heavy to lift but the Red Kite's wariness about landing in an unfamiliar situation means that it usually remains constantly alert to potential danger. It is likely that young and inexperienced birds, or individuals suffering from illness, or from lack of food, are most at risk.

The Red Kite's relatively low level of vulnerability to this threat is shown well by information on road mortalities of raptors and owls in Spain and eastern France (Muntaner & Mayol 1996, Baudvin 2003). In the Spanish study, a total of 18 Red Kites were found dead on roads during survey work, compared with 62 Buzzards, 749 Barn Owls and no fewer than 941 Little Owls. The particularly high figures for Barn and Little Owl partly reflect their large populations in Spain but, even when expressed as a proportion of relative population size, are higher than the figure for Red Kite. Barn Owl, Long-eared Owl and Buzzard were the most frequent victims in the French study, the latter no doubt because of its tendency to hunt from perches close to the edge of major roads. Eleven dead Red Kites were found during the ten years of this study compared to 538 Buzzards.

Red Kites are killed by collisions with road traffic but this is a far more frequent cause of mortality for species such as the Little Owl (above) and Barn Owl   *(Ian Carter)*

It is not only collisions with road traffic that results in this type of traumatic death. Trains have been involved in several incidents in Scotland (Brian Etheridge pers. comm.) including one bird found dead at the front of a train at Edinburgh station having presumably been carried some distance from where it was killed. There have also been several incidents in England, including two birds found on the same section of track in the Chilterns in April and May 2001. The railway worker who found these birds believed that they were attracted to the line to feed on Pheasants killed by passing trains. The vulnerability of young and inexperienced birds to collisions with moving objects is well shown by figures from Scotland. Of 15 birds killed by traffic (ten on roads and five on railways) since the start of the reintroduction programme, all except two were in their first year, and ten were killed within 13 weeks of leaving the nest (Brian Etheridge pers. comm.).

Aircraft have been involved in the death of several birds in Britain. Light aircraft using an airfield in central England have killed at least two adults as well as a recently-fledged young bird from a nest site in an adjacent wood. One of the adults was fatally injured by an aircraft soon after take-off. The pilot realised that he had collided with something and the unfortunate bird was retrieved during a subsequent search of the runway. In Wales, the cockpit window of a military jet was smashed as a result of a collision with a Red Kite, the bird being identified from feathers found inside the cockpit (Tony Cross pers. comm.).

Windfarms are becoming an increasingly familiar sight in many areas of Britain and are common in parts of the Red Kite's continental range, including in Germany and Spain. The risk to birds of prey from collision with wind turbines has been well documented by a large number of studies across the world. Despite their sharp eyesight, birds of prey are simply unable to follow the motion of the fast-moving rotors when flying close to the turbines and some collisions are therefore inevitable. Sites such as Tarifa in southern Spain and Altamont Pass in California have become well known for the large numbers of birds of prey killed by turbines (e.g. Percival 2000). Despite this, there remains a need for further research to determine the extent to which modern windfarms can impact on bird of prey populations. Initial work in Germany suggests that the Red Kite may be especially vulnerable to collision with turbines, no doubt because of its highly aerial lifestyle. Dürr and Langgemach (2006) reported that 16% of all bird casualties from turbines across Germany involved Red Kites, a total of 62 out of the 389 dead birds found. This is by no means the whole story as organised surveys are not carried out at the majority of windfarms and many deaths will therefore have gone unrecorded. The authors speculated that with more windfarms planned for Germany, impacts at the population level were possible in future. In Britain, two confirmed casualties have been found in recent years under wind turbines in Wales, both with part of a wing severed by the turbine blade. As in Germany, most incidents undoubtedly go unrecorded. A badly-needed research project is currently being carried out in central Scotland where a windfarm has been constructed in an area used by Red Kites from the reintroduced population. This study looked at Red Kite movements in the area before the windfarm was constructed and will continue to study flight lines and bird behaviour, aided by radio-tracking, now that the turbines are in place. The results of this 'before and after' study should be very useful in helping to assess the potential impact of windfarms on Red Kites and other raptors in Britain.

Surprisingly, given their excellent eyesight and highly manoeuvrable flight, Red Kites have, on rare occasions, also been recorded colliding with stationary objects, including trees, and even the side of a house in Wales. More surprising still was an event which was witnessed by visitors to the feeding station at Gigrin Farm in Wales. Two birds collided in mid-air resulting in the death of an adult female which 'dropped like a stone just feet in front of the hides' (Welsh Kite Trust Newsletter, Autumn 2001).

This unfortunate juvenile Red Kite was found fatally wounded at a windfarm near Aberystwyth, Wales in December 2003 *(Tony Cross)*

Other human factors

The trapping of birds of prey was formerly widespread in Britain and probably played an important role in the past decline of the Red Kite and other species. Larsen cage-traps are now used as a legal means of controlling Carrion/Hooded Crows and Magpies by exploiting the territorial behaviour of these species during the breeding season. A live 'call-bird' is placed in one compartment and when other birds of the same species arrive to chase it out of their territory they are caught in an adjacent compartment. Occasionally, gamekeepers have found raptors, including Red Kites, caught in these traps, particularly when they are baited with carrion in order to trap the first 'call-bird'. This should not present a major problem as it is a legal requirement to check such traps at least once every 24 hours and any non-target birds caught accidentally can then be released.

Red Kites occasionally become tangled up in refuse, either when foraging on rubbish dumps or, in the case of nestlings, as a result of material brought to the nest as decoration by the adults. One chick at a nest in southern England was found to have plastic wrapped so tightly around its leg that it had begun to cut into the flesh. It recovered fully following treatment but would not have been so lucky if the nest had not been visited and it had been left to fend for itself. Another chick, this time in northern Scotland, was found to have crawled inside a plastic bag in the nest when only 2-3 days old. It was freed and the plastic bag, together with other rubbish, removed from the nest. Once again, this chick probably only survived as a result of a timely visit to the nest site (Brian Etheridge pers. comm.). Full-grown birds can also become entangled in our carelessly-discarded rubbish, as with the individual found suspended by baler twine about 12m up in a tree near Gigrin Farm in Wales (Welsh Kite Trust Newsletter, Spring 2003). Another bird was found on the ground in Yorkshire unable to take off due to the mass of baler twine wrapped around its legs (Doug Simpson pers. comm.). As its name suggests, baler (or 'binder') twine is the coloured string used to tie bales of straw together. It poses a hazard to birds that pick it up because it separates easily into numerous thin but strong threads which can easily result in entanglement. Other human hazards which result in the occasional death include water troughs (a well known cause of death for Barn Owls) and livestock fences, with which birds can become entangled.

Natural mortality factors

Full-grown, healthy Red Kites have no serious predators other than humans, although they are occasionally attacked by large raptors such as Goshawk, Eagle Owl and the larger species of eagle. Unusually intense skirmishes with Buzzards, Ravens or rival Red Kites during the breeding season can also occasionally result in full-grown birds being killed. The nestlings are much more vulnerable and are taken by a range of opportunist avian and mammalian predators, especially if they are left unguarded by the parent birds (see Chapter 8).

The extent of losses resulting from natural causes such as disease is extremely difficult to quantify in wild birds, particularly in full-grown individuals, as, when birds feel unwell, they generally seek seclusion and cover, where they are less vulnerable to predators. The carcasses are therefore less likely to be found than is the case when birds are killed quickly by poisons or as a result of electrocution, for example. Even when a dead bird is recovered, the cause of death may still be difficult to determine, particularly if, as is often the case, several different factors are involved. Consider, for example, a Red Kite that contracts a disease and becomes gradually weaker until its ability to find food is restricted and it is at risk of starving to death. If food in the area is abundant and weather conditions are good then it has a chance of surviving until the worst effects of the disease have passed. If, however, the weather deteriorates, making foraging difficult, and food is in short supply, then it is much less likely to survive. A bird weakened by disease or hunger may be more likely to take risks such as scavenging on road kills, and it may become more susceptible to collisions or persecution due to a reduced fear of humans. A weakened bird is also more vulnerable to predation. In such cases, death is the result of a combination of different factors that are almost impossible to disentangle, however detailed the post-mortem that is carried out.

Various diseases have been recorded in both adult and nestling Red Kites in Britain. Infections caused by *Salmonella* and *E.* (*Escherichia*) *coli* bacteria have been found in Welsh chicks, which is perhaps not surprising, considering the putrefying meat that is sometimes brought to nests. It is not known whether Red Kites have any in-built resistance to such bacteria, as might be expected in a species that thrives on animal carrion. Red Kites found dead in Britain have also been diagnosed with diseases such as aspergillosis (a fungal infection), avian tuberculosis, avian pox (a skin disease) and trichomoniasis, and there are no doubt others that have yet to be recorded. Whether these infections regularly cause the death of otherwise healthy birds or affect mainly individuals already in poor condition is not known. A small number of nestlings in England have been diagnosed with metabolic bone disease by vets at the Zoological Society of London. This can result in numerous minor fractures and bone deformations which greatly reduce the affected bird's survival chances. It is likely that this is caused by poor diet and the feeding of unsuitable food to Red Kites by householders could be a contributory factor. Butchers' offcuts lack the calcium and other nutrients that are found in natural prey (when the whole animal is often consumed, including skin and bones) and this may result in poor growth and development (see Chapter 7).

Life expectancy and survival rates

The oldest Welsh Red Kite so far recorded was ringed 24 years before it died and there have been several other birds that have approached 20 years of age (Cross & Davis 1998, 2005). There are similar records from other parts of Europe, including a German bird found almost 26 years after it was first ringed.

In captivity, where there is no risk of premature death as a result of persecution, and a regular food supply is guaranteed, a Red Kite has lived for over 38 years (Newton 1979).

Studies of individually marked wing-tagged birds in Wales and young birds fitted with both wing-tags and radio-transmitters before release in England and Scotland, have provided very good information on annual survival rates. As with all species, young, and therefore inexperienced, birds are far more vulnerable than adults and this is reflected in lower survival rates. Combining the figures for released and wild-fledged birds in England in 1989-94, a minimum of 80% of birds survived their first year, rising to 94% in the second year and 95% for birds in their third year or older. In Scotland, survival rates were somewhat lower at 50% for first-year birds, rising to 88% for birds in their third year or older (Evans et al. 1999). More recently, survival rates for first-year birds in northern Scotland have dropped dramatically as a result of human persecution. It is estimated that only 5-10% of fledged young now survive to enter the breeding population at 2-3 years of age (Welsh Kite Trust Newsletter, Autumn 2005).

The lower survival rates for first-year birds relates not only to their lack of experience compared to adults but also to differences in behaviour. First-year birds often disperse away from the release site, leaving an area where local people are familiar with the species and levels of persecution are usually low. They may wander into areas where persecution is more common and so a higher proportion of these birds are likely to be killed. In contrast, adults are generally sedentary, and by remaining in the core breeding area, are less likely to fall victim to persecution. In order to calculate survival rates for first-year birds that did not disperse, released birds that remained in central England during their first winter, between the two main dispersal periods of autumn and spring, were considered (Carter & Grice 2000). Combining the figures for a number of years, this involved 43 individuals and, amazingly, all 43 survived the six-month period from October to March. The fact that the population at the time was still very small meant that levels of intraspecific competition for food were low which no doubt helps to explain such a high survival rate.

Survival rates in Wales were initially estimated as at least 60% for first-year birds, rising to 95% for territorial adults, based on re-sightings of wing-tagged birds (Newton et al. 1989), not dissimilar to the figures for birds reintroduced into more suitable lowland areas. More recent estimates, based on a higher number of sightings and recoveries, suggest that the adult survival rate is actually somewhat lower than this. Davis et al. (2001) calculated that 66% of birds survived their first year with 81% of older birds surviving from year to year. At least 41% of fledged young were known to have survived to breeding age, with the true figure probably between 45% and 50%. It is worth noting that the more rapid increase in the reintroduced populations in England and, in the early years, in Scotland, is mainly the result of far higher levels of breeding productivity and a reduced average age of first breeding, rather than higher survival rates for full-grown birds.

Red Kites have the potential to be very long-lived. It is a sad fact that, across much of its European range, survival rates are lower than they should be because many birds die prematurely at the hands of humans. The Red Kite is an adaptable bird and has the potential to thrive in our modern countryside. But it is also highly vulnerable to human persecution and the careless use of poisons, with the result that many populations are still in decline or struggling to recover from past reductions. The Red Kite was wiped out in many areas in the past when human attitudes towards birds of prey were sadly misguided as judged against modern standards. Its fate in the coming years will tell us much about the extent to which our attitudes have really changed.

SCIENTIFIC NAMES

Birds

American Black Vulture *Coragyps atratus*
Barn Owl *Tyto alba*
Bearded Vulture (Lammergeier) *Gypaetus barbatus*
Blackbird *Turdus merula*
Black-headed Gull *Larus ridibundus*
Black Kite *Milvus migrans*
Black-shouldered Kite *Elanus caeruleus*
Black Vulture *Aegypius monachus*
Booted Eagle *Hieraaetus pennatus*
Bullfinch *Pyrrhula pyrrhula*
(Common) Buzzard *Buteo buteo*
California Condor *Gymnogyps californianus*
Carrion Crow *Corvus corone*
Cattle Egret *Bubulcus ibis*
Chicken (Domestic Fowl) *Gallus* spp.
Cliff Swallow *Petrochelidon pyrrhonota*
Common Gull *Larus canus*
Coot *Fulica atra*
Corncrake *Crex crex*
Curlew *Numenius arquata*
Domestic/Feral Pigeon *Columba livia*
Eagle Owl *Bubo bubo*
Fulmar *Fulmarus glacialis*
Golden Eagle *Aquila chrysaetos*
Goshawk *Accipiter gentilis*
Great Bustard *Otis tarda*
Greylag Goose *Anser anser*
Grey Partridge *Perdix perdix*
Griffon Vulture *Gyps fulvus*
Gyr Falcon *Falco rusticolus*
Hen Harrier *Circus cyaneus*
(Grey) Heron *Ardea cinerea*
Hobby *Falco subbuteo*
Honey Buzzard *Pernis apivorus*
Hooded Crow *Corvus Cornix*
House Sparrow *Passer domesticus*

Imperial Eagle *Aquila adalberti*
Jackdaw *Corvus monedula*
Jay *Garrulus glandarius*
(Common) Kestrel *Falco tinnunculus*
Lanner Falcon *Falco biarmicus*
Lesser Black-backed Gull *Larus fuscus*
Lesser Kestrel *Falco naumanni*
Little Bustard *Tetrax tetrax*
Little Owl *Athene noctua*
Long-legged Buzzard *Buteo rufinus*
Magpie *Pica pica*
Mallard *Anas platyrhynchos*
Marsh Harrier *Circus aeruginosus*
Mississippi Kite *Ictinia mississippiensis*
Montagu's Harrier *Circus pygargus*
Moorhen *Gallinula chloropus*
Mute Swan *Cygnus olor*
Osprey *Pandion haliaetus*
Peregrine *Falco peregrinus*
(Common) Pheasant *Phasianus colchicus*
Raven *Corvus corax*
Red Grouse *Lagopus lagopus*
Red-legged Partridge *Alectoris rufa*
Robin *Erithacus rubecula*
Rook *Corvus frugilegus*
Rough-legged Buzzard *Buteo lagopus*
Skylark *Alauda arvensis*
Snail Kite *Rostrhamus sociabilis*
Song Thrush *Turdus philomelos*
Sparrowhawk *Accipiter nisus*
Starling *Sturnus vulgaris*
Tree Sparrow *Passer montanus*
Turkey Vulture *Cathartes aura*
Turtle Dove *Streptopelia turtur*
White Stork *Ciconia ciconia*
White-tailed Kite *Elanus leucurus*
White-tailed Sea Eagle *Haliaeetus albicilla*
Woodpecker *Picus/Dendrocopos* spp.
Woodpigeon *Columba palumbus*

Mammals
Badger *Meles meles*
Brown Rat *Rattus norvegicus*
Common Vole *Microtus arvalis*
Fallow Deer *Dama dama*
Field Vole *Microtus agrestis*
(Red) Fox *Vulpes vulpes*
(Common) Genet *Genetta genetta*
Grey Squirrel *Sciurus carolinensis*
(Common) Hamster *Cricetus cricetus*
(Brown) Hare *Lepus capensis*
Hedgehog *Erinaceus europaeus*
(Iberian) Lynx *Lynx pardina*
Mink *Mustela vison*
Mole *Talpa europaea*
Muntjac Deer *Muntiacus reevesi*
Pine Marten *Martes martes*
Polecat *Mustela putorius*
Rabbit *Oryctolagus cuniculus*
Red Squirrel *Sciurus vulgaris*
Roe Deer *Capreolus capreolus*
Stoat *Mustela erminea*
Water Vole *Arvicola terrestris*
Weasel *Mustela nivalis*
Wild Boar *Sus scrofa*
Wolf *Canis lupus*
Woodmouse *Apodemus sylvaticus*

Reptiles and amphibians
Common Frog *Rana temporaria*

Fish
Brown Trout *Salmo trutta*
Tench *Tinca tinca*

Plants
Ash *Fraxinus excelsior*
Beech *Fagus sylvatica*
English Oak *Quercus robur*

Field Maple *Acer campestre*
Larch *Larix* spp.
Norway Spruce *Picea abies*
Poplar *Populus* spp.
Scots Pine *Pinus sylvestris*
Sessile Oak *Quercus petraea*
Sycamore *Acer pseudoplatanus*
Turkey Oak *Quercus cerris*

BIBLIOGRAPHY

Adamski, A. 1995. Status, distribution and numbers of the Red Kite *Milvus milvus* in Poland. *Vogel und Umwelt* 8: 21-29.

Agombar, J. 2003. Post-fledging behaviour of the Red Kite in the East Midlands. *British Birds* 96: 88-89.

Ali, S. & Ripley, S.D. 1978. *Handbook of the Birds of India and Pakistan. Vol. 1.* (2nd Edition). Oxford University Press, Delhi.

Allavena, S., Fabbrizzi, F., Cecchi, R. & Galgano, R. 1996. Reintroduction of the Red Kite *Milvus milvus* in Tuscany, Italy. In: Pandolfi, M. (ed.) *Abstracts of the 2nd International Conference on Raptors*, 65. Urbino, Italy.

Angelini, J., Tanferna, A., Bulgarini, F. & Pandolfi, M. 2001. Reintroduction of Red Kite *Milvus milvus* in Gola Della Rossa Regional Park (Italy) and first radio-tracking data of released birds. *Abstracts for 4th Eurasian Congress on Raptors*, 6-7. Raptor Research Foundation, Seville.

Bainbridge, I.P., Evans, R.J., Broad, R.A., Crooke, C.H., Duffy, K., Green, R.E., Love, J.A. & Mudge, G.P. 2003. Reintroduction of White-tailed Eagles (*Haliaeetus albicilla*) to Scotland. In: Thompson, D.B.A., Redpath, S.M., Fielding, A.H., Marquiss, M. & Galbraith, C.A. (eds.) *Birds of Prey in a Changing Environment*, 393-406. Scottish Natural Heritage, Edinburgh.

Baker, K. 1993. *Identification Guide to European Non-Passerines.* British Trust for Ornithology Guide 24. BTO, Thetford.

Barton, N.W.H. & Houston, D.C. 1993. A comparison of digestive efficiency in birds of prey. *Ibis* 135: 363-371.

Baudvin, H. 2003. Motorway mortality of birds of prey and owls in eastern France. In: Chancellor, R.D. & Meyburg, B.-U. (eds.) *Raptors Worldwide: Proceedings of the VI World Conference on Birds of Prey and Owls*, 787-793. World Working Group on Birds of Prey and Owls/Birdlife Hungary, Budapest.

Beguin, J. 1983. *Report on the chemical control of voles.* The Department of Agriculture of the Republic and Canton of Neuchatel, Neuchatel.

Bergier, P. 1987. Les rapaces diurnes du Maroc. *Annales du CEEP*, 3. Aix en Provence.

Berlijn, M. 2003. Western Palearctic news (reports from The Netherlands). *Birding World* 16: 232.

Bevanger, K. & Overskaug, K. 1998. Utility structures as a mortality factor for raptors and owls in Norway. In: Chancellor, R.D., Meyburg, B.-U. & Ferrero, J.J. (eds.) *Holarctic Birds of Prey: Proceedings of an International Conference*, 381-392. ADENEX/WWGBP, Calamonte, Spain.

Bijleveld, M. 1974. *Birds of Prey in Europe*. The Macmillan Press Ltd, London.

BirdLife International. 2004. *Birds in Europe: population estimates, trends and conservation status*. Birdlife Conservation Series No. 12. Birdlife International, Cambridge.

Birkhead, T.R. 1991. *The magpies: The ecology and behaviour of Black-billed and Yellow-billed Magpies*. Poyser, London.

Blanco, J.C. 1982. *Ecología trófica invernal del Milano Real* Milvus milvus *en Doñana*. Tesis de Licenciatura. Universidad de Oviedo.

Blanco, J.C. & González, J.L. 1992. *El Libro Rojo de los Vertebrados de España*. ICONA, Madrid.

Blanco, J.C., González, J.L. & Hiraldo, F. 1990a. Trophic and spatial relationships between wintering Red Kites *Milvus milvus* and Marsh Harriers *Circus aeruginosus* in the Guadalquivir marshes. *Journal of Miscellaneous Zoology* 14: 161-166.

Blanco, J.C., Hiraldo, F. & Heredia, B. 1990b. Variations in the diet and foraging behaviour of a wintering Red Kite *Milvus milvus* population in response to changes in food availability. *Ardeola* 37: 267-278.

Bolam, G. 1912. *Birds of Northumberland and the Eastern Borders*. Henry Hunter Blair, Alnwick.

Brown, A. & Grice, P. 2005. *Birds in England*. Poyser, London.

Brown, L. 1970. *Eagles*. Arthur Barker, London.

Buckley, N.J. 1997. Experimental tests of the information-center hypothesis with Black Vultures *Coragyps atratus* and Turkey Vultures *Cathartes aura*. *Behavioural Ecology and Sociobiology* 41: 267-279.

Bustamante, J. 1993. Post-fledging dependence period and development of flight and hunting behaviour in the Red Kite *Milvus milvus*. *Bird Study* 40: 181-188.

Bustamante, J. 1994. Family break-up in Black and Red Kites *Milvus migrans* and *M. milvus*: is time of independence an offspring decision? *Ibis* 136: 176-184.

Bustamante, J. & Hiraldo, F. 1990. Adoptions of fledglings by Black and Red Kites. *Animal Behaviour* 39: 804-806.

Bustamante, J. & Hiraldo, F. 1993. The function of aggressive chases by breeding Black and Red Kites *Milvus migrans* and *M. milvus* during the post-fledging dependence period. *Ibis* 135: 139-147.

Cadbury, J. 1991. *Persecution: birds of prey and owls killed in the UK, 1979-1989*. RSPB/Nature Conservancy Council.

Cade, T.J. 2000. Progress in translocation of diurnal raptors. In: Chancellor, R.D. & Meyburg, B.-U. (eds.) *Raptors at Risk: Proceedings of the V World Conference on Birds of Prey and Owls*, 343-372. World Working Group on Birds of Prey and Owls, Berlin.

Campbell, B. & Lack, E. (eds.) 1985. *A Dictionary of Birds.* Poyser, Calton.

Cardiel, I. 2006. *El Milano Real en España: II censo nacional (2004).* SEO/Birdlife International, Madrid.

Carter, I. 1998. The changing fortunes of the Red Kite in Suffolk. *Suffolk Birds* 46: 6-10.

Carter, I. 2001. The role of reintroductions in conserving British birds. *The Transactions of the Suffolk Naturalists' Society* 37: 8-13.

Carter, I. 2003. Return of the Red Kite. *Biologist* 50(5): 217-221.

Carter, I. 2005. The benefits and dangers of species reintroductions: Lessons from the Red Kite reintroduction programme and other bird reintroductions. In: Rooney, P., Noland, P. & Hill, D. (eds.) *Restoration, Reintroduction and Translocation: Proceedings of the 20th Conference of the Institute of Ecology and Environmental Management*, 117-122. IEEM, Winchester.

Carter, I. & Burn, A. 2000. Problems with rodenticides: The threat to Red Kites and other wildlife. *British Wildlife* 11: 192-197.

Carter, I. & Grice, P. 2000. Studies of re-established Red Kites in England. *British Birds* 93: 304-322.

Carter, I. & Grice, P. 2002. *The Red Kite Reintroduction Programme in England.* English Nature Research Reports 451. English Nature, Peterborough.

Carter, I. & Newbery, P. 2004. Reintroduction as a tool for population recovery of farmland birds. In: Vickery, J.A., Evans, A.D., Grice, P.V., Aebischer, N.J. & Brand-Hardy, R. (eds.) *Ecology and Conservation of Lowland Farmland Birds II: The Road to Recovery. Ibis* 146 (Suppl. 2): 221-229.

Carter, I. & Whitlow, G. 2005. *Red Kites in the Chilterns (2nd Edition).* English Nature/Chilterns Conservation Board, Princes Risborough.

Carter, I., Evans, I. & Crockford, N. 1995. The Red Kite re-introduction project in Britain – progress so far and future plans. *British Wildlife* 7: 18-25.

Carter, I., McQuaid, M., Snell, N. & Stevens, P. 1999. The Red Kite *Milvus milvus* reintroduction project: Modelling the impact of translocating Red Kite young within England. *Journal of Raptor Research* 33: 251-254.

Carter, I., Cross, A.V., Douse, A., Duffy, K., Etheridge, B., Grice, P.V., Newbery, P., Orr-Ewing, D.C., O'Toole, L., Simpson, D. & Snell, N. 2003. Re-introduction and conservation of the Red Kite *Milvus milvus* in Britain: Current threats and prospects for future range expansion. In: Thompson, D.B.A., Redpath, S.M., Fielding, A.H., Marquiss, M. & Galbraith, C.A. (eds.)

Birds of Prey in a Changing Environment, 407-416. Scottish Natural Heritage, Edinburgh.

Cayford, J.T. & Percival, S.M. 1992. Barn Owl captive breeding and release in Britain. *New Scientist* 1087: 29-33.

Clarke, R. 1996. *Montagu's Harrier.* Arlequin Press, Chelmsford.

Clements, R. 2002. The Common Buzzard in Britain: A new population estimate. *British Birds* 95: 377-383.

Cocker, M. & Mabey, R. 2005. *Birds Britannica.* Chatto & Windus, London.

Collar, N.J. & Andrew, A. 1988. *Birds to watch: The ICBP world check-list of threatened birds.* ICBP Technical Publication 8, Cambridge.

Conzemius, T. 1998. Revierkartierung der 'Territorialen Saison-Population' des Rotmilans *Milvus milvus* 1997 in Luxembourg. *Regulus Wiss. Ber.* 17: 1-26.

Cordero, P.J., Evans, I.M., Parkin, D.T. & Galbraith, C.A. 1997. Studies of the genetics of a naturalised population of Red Kites *Milvus milvus* in England established by translocation. In: Tew, T.E., Crawford, T.J., Spencer, J.W., Stevens, D.P., Usher, M.B. & Warren, J. (eds.) *The Role of Genetics in Conserving Small Populations*, 89-96. JNCC, Peterborough.

Corso, A. 2002. Separation of Black Kite from Red Kite: the pitfall of the eastern form and rufous variants. *Birding World* 15: 248-252.

Corso, A., Palumbo, G., Manzi, A., Salerno, M., Sanna, M. & Carafa, M. 1999. Risultati preliminary dell'indagine nazionale sul nibbio reale *Milvus milvus* svernante in Italia. *Avocetta* 23: 12.

Cramp, S. & Simmons, K.E.L. (eds.) 1980. *The Birds of the Western Palearctic, Vol. II.* Oxford University Press, Oxford.

Crease, A.J. 1998. Red Kite fishing like Osprey. *British Birds* 91: 592.

Crochet, P-A. 2006a. Recent DNA studies of kites: what was Cape Verde Kite and does it still exist? *Birding World* 18: 486.

Crochet, P-A. 2006b. The systematic status of Yellow-billed Kite. *Birding World* 18: 487-488.

Cromie, R.L., Brown, M.J., Hughes, B., Hoccom, D.G. & Williams, G. 2002. Prevalence of lead shot pellets in Mallard purchased from game dealers in England in winter 2001/02. In: *Compliance with the Lead Shot Regulations (England).* Unpublished RSPB report.

Cross, A.V. & Davis, P.E. 1998 (revised edition 2005). *The Red Kite of Wales.* The Welsh Kite Trust, Llandrindod Wells.

D'Arcy, G. 1999. *Ireland's Lost Birds.* Four Court's Press, Dublin.

Davies, C. 2002. The European Bird Report. *British Birds* 95: 174-188.

Davis, P. 1993. The Red Kite in Wales: setting the record straight. *British Birds* 86: 295-298.

Davis, P.E. & Davis, J.E. 1981. The food of the Red Kite in Wales. *Bird Study* 28: 33-44.

Davis, P.E. & Newton, I. 1981. Population and breeding of Red Kites in Wales over a 30-year period. *Journal of Animal Ecology* 50: 759-772.

Davis, P., Cross, A.V. & Davis, J. 2001. Movement, settlement, breeding and survival of Red Kites *Milvus milvus* marked in Wales. *Welsh Birds* 3: 18-43.

Dawson, M.J. 1988. *The Red Kite* Milvus milvus: *Nesting sites, old and new, in Great Britain.* Oriel Stringer, Brighton.

Delibes, M. & García, L. 1984. Hábitos alimenticios del Milano Real en Doñana durante el periodo de cria. *Ardeola* 31: 115-121.

Dennis, R. 1996. *A proposal to translocate Ospreys to Rutland Water* [also annual project progress reports]. Anglian Water and Leicestershire and Rutland Trust for Nature Conservation.

Dixon, W.J.B. 2001. *A study of the reintroduced population of Red Kite* Milvus milvus *in southern England.* Unpublished PhD thesis, Oxford University.

Dürr, T. & Langgemach, T. 2006. [Wind turbines as a mortality factor for birds of prey]. *Populationsökologie Greifvögel- und Eulenarten* 5: 483-490. [In German with English summary].

Eden, P. 2002. *Haematological changes with disease in Red Kites with particular reference to lead poisoning.* Unpublished MSc thesis. Institute of Zoology, London.

Encalado, J.J.R. 1998. Red Kites 'playing' with newspaper. *British Birds* 91: 233-234.

Evans, I.M. & Pienkowski, M.W. 1991. World status of the Red Kite: A background to the experimental reintroduction to England and Scotland. *British Birds* 84: 171-187.

Evans, I.M., Dennis, R.H., Orr-Ewing, D.C., Kjellén, N., Andersson, P-O., Sylvén, M., Senosiain, A. & Carbo, F.C. 1997. The re-establishment of Red Kite breeding populations in Scotland and England. *British Birds* 90: 123-138.

Evans, I.M., Cordero, P.J. & Parkin, D.T. 1998. Successful breeding at one year of age by Red Kites *Milvus milvus* in southern England. *Ibis* 140: 53-57.

Evans, I.M., Summers, R.W., O'Toole, L., Orr-Ewing, D.C., Evans, R., Snell, N. & Smith, J. 1999. Evaluating the success of translocating Red Kites *Milvus milvus* to the UK. *Bird Study* 46: 129-144.

Ferguson-Lees, J. & Christie, D.A. 2001. *Raptors of the World*. Christopher Helm, London.

Fisher, J. 1947. *Natural history of the Kite*. RSPB Annual Report, 1947.

Forsman, D. 1999. *The Raptors of Europe and the Middle East: A Handbook of Field Identification*. Poyser, London.

Forsman, D. 2003. Identification of Black-eared Kite. *Birding World* 16: 156-160.

Gaibani, G., Aradis, A., Pandolfi, M., Perna, P. & Cataudella, R. 2001. Monitorig the Red Kite *Milvus milvus* population of Parco Nazionale del Pollino: Preliminary data. *Abstracts of the 4th Eurasian Congress on Raptors*, 71. Raptor Research Foundation, Seville.

Gamauf, A. 1995. Schwarzmilan und Rotmilan in Österreich: Populationsentwicklung und verbreitung. In: Richarz, K., Meyburg, B.-U. & Hormann, M. (eds.) Rotmilan-Sonderheft, 29-38. *Vogel und Umwelt*, Bd. 8. [In German with English summary].

García, J.T., Viñuela, J. & Sunyer, C. 1998. Geographic variation of the winter diet of the Red Kite *Milvus milvus* in the Iberian Peninsula. *Ibis* 140: 302-309.

Garzón, J. 1974. Contribución al estudio del estatus, alimentación y protección de las Falconiformes en España central. *Ardeola* 19: 279-330.

Geeson, J. & Geeson, J. 1990. First Red Kite record for The Gambia. *Malimbus* 11: 144.

George, K. 1994. Zur Überwinterung des Rotmilans *Milvus milvus* im nördlichen Harzvorland (Sachsen-Anhalt). *Vogelwelt* 115: 127-132.

George, K. 1995. Überwinterung von Rotmilanen *Milvus milvus* im nördlichen Harzvorland/Sachsen-Anhalt. In: Richarz, K., Meyburg, B.-U. & Hormann, M. (eds.) Rotmilan-Sonderheft, 59-66. *Vogel und Umwelt*, Bd. 8. [In German with English summary].

Gilbert, H.A. 1957. Spanish Kites in Radnorshire. *The Field* (December issue). Reproduced in Welsh Kite Trust Newsletter 9, Spring 2001: 11-12.

Glutz von Blotzheim, U., Bauer, K.M. & Bezzel, E. 1971. *Handbuch der Vögel Mitteleuropas, vol 4*. Frankfurt-am-Main.

Gómez-Tejedor, H. 1998. Comportamiento cleptoparásito del Milano Real *Milvus milvus* en un vertedero. In: Chancellor, R.D., Meyburg, B.-U. & Ferrero, J.J. (eds.) *Holarctic Birds of Prey: Proceedings of an International Conference*, 173-176. World Working Group on Birds of Prey and Owls/ADENEX, Calamonte, Spain. [In Spanish with English summary].

González, L.M. 1989. *Historia natural del Aguila Imperial Ibérica* Aquila adalberti: *taxonomía, población, análisis de la distribución, alimentación,* *reproducción y conservación*. Doctoral thesis, Universidad Autónoma de Madrid.

Gottschalk, T. 1995. Zugbeobachtungen am Rotmilan im Hinblick auf Zugverlauf und Zuggeschwindigkeit im Vortaunus/Hessen. In: Richarz, K., Meyburg, B.-U. & Hormann, M. (eds.) Rotmilan-Sonderheft, 47-52. *Vogel und Umwelt*, Bd. 8. [In German with English summary].

Gowland, C.H. 1947. The Natural History of the Kite. *Bird Land* 2: 364-367.

Green, B.H. 1979. *Wildlife Introductions to Great Britain*. Report by the Working Group on Introductions of the UK Committee for International Nature Conservation (1979). Nature Conservancy Council, London.

Grell, M.B. 2003. *Forslag til en forvaltningsplan for bevarelsen af Rod Glente Milvus milvus i Danmark*. Dansk Ornitologisk Forening. [In Danish with English summary].

Hagemeijer, W.J.M. & Blair, M.J. (eds.) 1997. *The EBCC Atlas of European Breeding Birds: Their distribution and abundance*. Poyser, London.

Hardy, J., Crick, H.Q.P., Wernham, C.V., Riley, H.T., Etheridge, B. & Thompson, D.B.A. 2006. *Raptors: A field guide to survey and monitoring*. The Stationary Office, Edinburgh.

Harvie-Brown, J.A. 1906. *A fauna of the Tay Basin and Strathmore*. David Douglas, Edinburgh.

Hazevoet, C.J. 1995. *The Birds of the Cape Verde Islands*. British Ornithologists Union, Tring.

Heredia, B., Alonso, J.C. & Hiraldo, F. 1991. Space and habitat use by Red Kites *Milvus milvus* during winter in the Guadalquivir marshes: a comparison between resident and wintering populations. *Ibis* 133: 374-381.

Hernández, M. 1997. *Preliminary report on the illegal poisoning of birds of prey in Spain, September 1995-April 1997*. Laboratorio Forense de Vida Silvestre, Madrid.

Hille, S. 1995a. *Untersuchungen zur Ökologie des Rotmilans* Milvus milvus *in der Rhön*. Masters Thesis, University of Giessen.

Hille, S. 1995b. Nahrungswahl und Jagdstrategien des Rotmilans *Milvus milvus* im Biosphärenreservat Rhön/Hessen. In: Richarz, K., Meyburg, B.-U. & Hormann, M. (eds.) Rotmilan-Sonderheft, 99-126. *Vogel und Umwelt*, Bd. 8. [In German with English summary].

Hille, S. 1998. Zur situation der Milane *Milvus milvus fasciicauda* (Hartert, 1914) und *Milvus m. migrans* (Boddaert, 1783) auf den Kapverdischen Inseln. *Journal of Ornithology* 139: 73-75. [In German with English summary].

Hiraldo, F., Heredia, B. & Alonso, J.C. 1993. Communal roosting of wintering Red Kites *Milvus milvus*: Social feeding strategies for the exploitation of food resources. *Ethology* 93: 117-124.

Holloway, S. 1996. *The Historical Atlas of Breeding Birds in Britain and Ireland*: 1875-1900. Poyser, London.

Holmes, J., Walker, D., Davies, P. & Carter, I. 2000. *The illegal persecution of raptors in England*. English Nature Research Report No. 343. English Nature, Peterborough.

Holmes, J., Carter, I., Stott, M., Hughes, J., Davies, P. & Walker, D. 2003. Raptor persecution in England at the end of the twentieth century. In: Thompson, D.B.A., Redpath, S.M., Fielding, A.H., Marquiss, M. & Galbraith, C.A. (eds.) *Birds of Prey in a Changing Environment*, 481-485. Scottish Natural Heritage, Edinburgh.

Image, B. 1992. Montagu's Harriers taking prey disturbed by farm machinery. *British Birds* 85: 559.

Inskipp, C. & Inskipp, T. 1991. *A Guide to the Birds of Nepal* (2nd Edition). Christopher Helm, London.

IUCN. 1995. *Guidelines for Re-introductions* - www.iucn.org/themes/ssc/publications/policy/reinte.htm

James, P. (ed.) 1996. *Birds of Sussex*. Sussex Ornithological Society.

Janss, G.F.E. 2000. Avian mortality from power lines: a morphologic approach of a species-specific mortality. *Biological Conservation* 95: 353-359.

JNCC. 2003. *A policy for conservation translocations of species in Britain*. Joint Nature Conservation Committee, Peterborough.

Johnson, J.A., Watson, R.T. & Mindell, D.P. 2005. Prioritising species conservation: Does the Cape Verde Kite exist? *Proceedings of the Royal Society B* 272: 1365-1371.

Jonsson, L. 1992. *Birds of Europe: with North Africa and the Middle East*. Christopher Helm, London.

Jordano, P. 1981. Relaciones interspecificas y coexistencia entre el Águila Real *Aquila Chrysaetos* y el Águila Perdicera *Hieraaetus fasciatus* en Sierra Morena central. *Ardeola* 28: 67-87.

Jørgensen, H.E. 1989. *Danmarks Rovfugle*. Copenhagen.

Juillard, M. 1977. Observations sur l'hivernage et les dorloirs du Milard Royal *Milvus milvus* dans le nord-ouest de la Suisse. *Nos Oiseaux* 34: 41-57.

Kalaher, M. 2005. *Breeding Red Kites, 2004*. In: Sussex Bird Report for 2004.

Kenward, R. 2006. *The Goshawk*. Poyser, London.

Kjellén, N. 1992. Differential timing of autumn migration between sex and age groups in raptors at Falsterbo, Sweden. *Ornis Scandinavica* 23: 420-434.

Kjellén, N. 1994. Differences in age and sex ratio among migrating and wintering raptors in southern Sweden. *The Auk* 111(2): 274-284.

Kjellén, N. 1996. Project Glada-Årsrapport 1995. [The Red Kite Project 1995] *Anser* 35: 17-25. [In Swedish with English summary].

Kjellén, N. 1999. Project Glada-Årsrapport 1998. [The Red Kite Project 1998] *Anser* 38: 85-89. [In Swedish with English summary].

Larraz, D.S. 1999. Dumps for dead livestock and the conservation of wintering Red Kites *Milvus milvus*. *Journal of Raptor Research* 33: 338-340.

Latham, J. 1821-1828. *A General History of Birds*, II vols. Privately published, Winchester.

Lilford, Lord. 1880-1883. *Notes on the Birds of Northamptonshire Vol. 1*. Taylor & Francis, London.

Lockie, J.D., Ratcliffe, D.A. & Balharry, R. 1969. Breeding success and organochlorine residues in Golden Eagles in west Scotland. *Journal of Applied Ecology* 6: 381-389.

Lovegrove, R. 1990. *The Kite's Tale: The story of the Red Kite in Wales*. RSPB, Sandy.

Lovegrove, R. 2007. *Silent Fields: The long decline of a nation's wildlife*. Oxford University Press, Oxford.

Lovegrove, R., Elliot, G. & Smith, K. 1990. The Red Kite in Britain. *RSPB Conservation Review* 4: 15-21. RSPB, Sandy.

Macleod, R.D. 1954. *Key to the names of British birds*. Sir Isaac Pitman & Sons Ltd, London.

Mammen, U. & Opitz, H. 2000. *Vogel des Jahres 2000: Der Rotmilan*. NABU, Bonn.

Mammen, U. & Stubbe, M. 1995. Alterseinschätzung und brutbeginn des Rotmilans *Milvus milvus*. In: Richarz, K., Meyburg, B.-U. & Hormann, M. (eds.) Rotmilan-Sonderheft, 91-98. *Vogel und Umwelt*, Bd. 8. [In German with English summary].

Mañosa, S. 2002. *The conflict between gamebird hunting and raptors in Europe*. Unpublished report from Reconciling Gamebird Hunting and Biodiversity (REGHAB) project to European Commission, Brussels.

Marchant, J.H. & Gregory, R.D. 1999. Numbers of nesting Rooks *Corvus frugilegus* in the United Kingdom in 1996. *Bird Study* 46: 258-273.

Marzluff, J.M., Heinrich, B. & Marzluff, C.S. 1996. Raven roosts are mobile information centres. *Animal Behaviour* 51: 89-103.

May, C.A., Wetton, J.H. & Parkin, D.T. 1993a. Polymorphic sex-specific sequences in birds of prey. *Proceedings of the Royal Society of London B* 253: 271-276.

May, C.A., Wetton, J.H., Davis, P.E., Brookfield, J.F.Y. & Parkin, D.T. 1993b. Single-locus profiling reveals loss of variation in inbred populations of the Red Kite *Milvus milvus*. *Proceedings of the Royal Society of London B* 251: 165-170.

Mebs, T. 1995. Die besondere Verantwortung der Mitteleuropäer für den rotmilan – status und bestandsentwicklung. In: Richarz, K., Meyburg, B.-U. & Hormann, M. (eds.) Rotmilan-Sonderheft, 7-10. *Vogel und Umwelt*, Bd. 8. [In German with English summary].

Medina, M. 2000. *Studies of a breeding pair of Red Kites in central England.* Unpublished MSc thesis, Anglia Polytechnic University, Cambridge.

Meretsky, V.J., Snyder, N.F.R., Beissinger, S.R., Clendenen, D.A. & Wiley, J.W. 1999. Demography of the California Condor: Implications for re-establishment. *Conservation Biology* 14: 957-967.

Meyburg, B.-U. & Meyburg, C. 1987. *Present status of diurnal birds of prey in various countries bordering the Mediterranean.* Instituto Nazionale di Biologia della Selvagina XII. Bologne.

Minns, D. & Gilbert, D. 2001. *Red Kites - Naturally Scottish.* Scottish Natural Heritage, Battleby.

Mitchell, F.S. 1892. *The Birds of Lancashire.* Gurney & Jackson, London.

Mock, D.W., Lamey, T.C. & Thomson, D.B.A. 1988. Falsifiability and the Information Center Hypothesis. *Ornis Scandinavia* 19: 231-248.

Montagu, G. 1833. *Ornithological Dictionary of British Birds.* Orr & Smith, London.

Mosimann, P. & Juillard, M. 1988. Brutbestand und winterverbreitung des Rotmilans *Milvus milvus* in der Schweiz. *Orn. Beobachter* 85: 199-206.

Mougeot, F. 2000. Territorial intrusions and copulation patterns in Red Kites *Milvus milvus* in relation to breeding density. *Animal Behaviour* 59: 633-642.

Mougeot, F. & Bretagnolle, V. 2006. Breeding biology of the Red Kite *Milvus milvus* in Corsica. *Ibis* 148: 436-448.

Müller, W. 1995. Brut-und winterbestand des Rotmilans *Milvus milvus* in der Schweiz. In: Richarz, K., Meyburg, B.-U. & Hormann, M. (eds.) Rotmilan-Sonderheft, 39-45. *Vogel und Umwelt*, Bd. 8. [In German with English summary].

Muntaner, J. & Mayol, J. (eds.) 1996. *Biology and Conservation of Mediterranean Raptors, 1994.* SEO Monographía No. 4, Madrid. [In Spanish with English summary].

Nachtigall, W., Stubbe, M. & Herrmann, S. 2003. Aktionsraum und habitat-nutzung des Rotmilans *Milvus milvus* im winter: Eine telemetrische studie im Nordharzvorland. *Journal für Ornithologie* 144: 284-294. [In German with English summary].

Newton, I. 1979. *Population Ecology of Raptors*. Poyser, London.

Newton, I., Davis, P.E. & Moss, D. 1981. Distribution and breeding of Red Kites in relation to land-use in Wales. *Journal of Applied Ecology* 18: 173-186.

Newton, I., Davis, P.E. & Davis, J.E. 1989. Age of first breeding, dispersal and survival of Red Kites *Milvus milvus* in Wales. *Ibis* 131: 16-21.

Newton, I., Davis, P.E. & Moss, D. 1994. Philopatry and population growth of Red Kites *Milvus milvus* in Wales. *Proceedings of the Royal Society of London B* 257: 317-323.

Newton, I., Davis, P.E. & Moss, D. 1996. Distribution and breeding of Red Kites *Milvus milvus* in relation to afforestation and other land-use in Wales. *Journal of Applied Ecology* 33: 210-224.

Newton, I., Shore, R.F., Wyllie, I., Birds, J.D.S. & Dale, L. 1999. Empir-ical evidence of side-effects of rodenticides on some predatory birds and mammals. In: Cowand, D.P. & Feare, C.J. (eds.) *Advances in vertebrate pest management*, 347-367. Filander Verlag, Fürth.

Nikiforov, M.E. 1996. European News. *British Birds* 89: 29.

Nisbet, I.C.T. 1959. The Kites of Sixteenth-century London. *British Birds* 52: 239-240.

Ntampakis, D. 2003. *Food preferences of the Red Kite and the rodenticide problem*. Unpublished MSc thesis, University of Reading.

Ntampakis, D. & Carter, I. 2005. Red Kites and rodenticides - a feeding experiment. *British Birds* 98: 411-416.

Orr-Ewing, D.C., Duffy, K., O'Toole, L., Stubbe, M. & Schönbrodt, R. 2006. Final report on the translocation of Red Kites *Milvus milvus* from Germany to central Scotland. *Populationsökologie Greifvögel- und Eulenarten* 5: 261-272.

Ortlieb, R. 1989. *Der Rotmilan* Milvus milvus. Die Neue Brehm-Bücherei 532, Wittenburg.

O'Toole, L., Fielding, A.H. & Haworth, P.F. 2002. Reintroduction of the Golden Eagle into the Republic of Ireland. *Biological Conservation* 103: 303-312.

Ottway, D. 2002. *The functional significance of semi-colonial nest spacing and communal roosting in the Red Kite* Milvus milvus. Unpublished MSc thesis. Anglia Polytechnic University, Cambridge.

Pain, D.J., Amiard-Triquet, C., Bavoux, C., Burneleau, G., Eon, L. & Nicolau-Guillaumet, P. 1993. Lead poisoning in wild populations of Marsh Harriers *Circus aeruginosus* in the Camargue and Charente-Maritime, France. *Ibis* 135: 379-386.

Pain, D.J., Carter, I., Sainsbury, A.W., Shore, R.F., Eden, P., Taggart, M.A., Konstantinos, S., Walker, L.A., Meharg, A.A. & Raab, A. 2007. Lead contamination and associated disease in captive and reintroduced Red Kites *Milvus milvus* in England. *Science of the Total Environment* 376: 116-127.

Pain, D.J., Sears, J. & Newton, I. 1995. Lead concentrations in birds of prey in Britain. *Environmental Pollution* 87: 173-180.

Palin, S. 2002. *Pickcheese, billy wise and cobble: Illustrated folk names of birds.* Taghan Press, East Ruston.

Palmer, P. 2000. *First for Britain and Ireland: A historical account of birds new to Britain and Ireland 1600-1999.* Arlequin Press, Chelmsford.

Patrimonio, O. 1990. *Le Milan Royal* Milvus milvus *en Corse: répartition et reproduction.* Travaux Scientifiques du Parc Naturel Régional et des Réserves Naturelles de Corse.

Percival, S.M. 2000. Birds and wind turbines in Britain. *British Wildlife* 12: 8-13.

Petty, S.J. 1989. *Goshawks: Their status, requirements and management.* Forestry Commission Bulletin 81. HMSO, London.

Porstendörfer, D. 1997. Untersuchungen zum aktionsraum des Rotmilans *Milvus milvus* während der Jungenaufzucht. *Vogelkdl. Ber. Niedersachs.* 30: 15-17.

Ratcliffe, D. 1993. *The Peregrine Falcon (second edition).* Poyser, London.

Ratcliffe, D. 1997. *The Raven: A natural history in Britain and Ireland.* Poyser, London.

Reid-Henry, D. & Harrison, C. 1988. *The History of the Birds of Britain.* Collins, London.

Rheinwald, G. 1982. *Brutvogelatlas der Bundesrepublik Deutschland-Kartierung 1980.* Schriftenreihe des Dachverbandes Deutscher Avifaunisten.

Richmond, W.K. 1959. *British Birds of Prey.* Lutterworth, London.

Roberts, S.J., Lewis, J.M.S. & Williams, I.T. 1999. Breeding European Honey-Buzzards in Britain. *British Birds* 92: 326-345.

Rocamora, G. & Yeatmann-Berthelot, D. 1999. *Oiseaux menacés et à surveiller en France.* SEOF/LPO, Paris.

Roques, S. & Negro, J.J. 2005. Mitochondrial DNA genetic diversity and population history of a dwindling raptorial bird, the Red Kite *Milvus milvus*. *Biological Conservation* 126: 41-50.

Rufino, R., Araüjo, A. & Abreu, M. 1985. Breeding raptors in Portugal: distribution and population estimates. In: Newton, I. & Chancellor, R.D. (eds.) *Conservation Studies on Raptors*. ICBP Technical Publication 5: 3-14. Cambridge.

Sagot, F. 1991. Milan Royal *Milvus milvus*. In: Yeatmann-Berthelot, D. & Jarry, G. (eds.) *Atlas des oiseaux de France en hiver*, 146-147. Société Ornithologique de France, Paris.

Sarker, S.U. & Sarker, K. 1985. Birds of prey and their conservation in the Sundarbans Mangrove Forests, Khulna, Bangladesh. In: Newton, I. & Chancellor, R.D. (eds.) *Conservation Studies on Raptors. ICBP Technical Publication* 5: 205-209. Cambridge.

Schmid, H., Luder, R., Naef-Daenzer, B., Graf, R. & Zbinden, N. 1998. *Atlas des oiseaux nicheurs de Suisse. Distribution des oiseaux nicheurs en Suisse et en Liechtenstein en 1993-1996*. Station Ornithologique Suisse, Sempach.

Scott, D. 2002. *Attempted nesting of the Red Kite* Milvus milvus *in Northern Ireland during 2002*. Welsh Kite Trust Newsletter 12, Autumn 2002: 16-17.

Scottish Ornithologists Club. 2003. *Scottish raptor monitoring report 2003*. SOC, Aberlady.

Seoane, J., Viñuela, J., Díaz-Delgado, R. & Bustamante, J. 2003. The effects of land use and climate on Red Kite distribution in the Iberian peninsula. *Biological Conservation* 111: 401-414.

Sergio, F., Blas, J., Forero, M., Fernández, N., Donázar, J.A. & Hiraldo, F. 2005. Preservation of wide-ranging top predators by site-protection: Black and Red Kites in Doñana National Park. *Biological Conservation* 125: 11-21.

Sharp, E.A. & Hunter, K. 1999. *The occurrence of second generation anticoagulant rodenticide residues in Red Kites in Scotland*. Scottish Agricultural Science Agency, unpublished report.

Sharrock, J.T.R. & Davies, C. 2000. The European Bird Report: Non-passerines, including near-passerines. *British Birds* 93: 114-128.

Shawyer, C. 1998. *The Barn Owl*. Arlequin Press, Chelmsford.

Shore, R.F., Birks, J.D.S., Freestone, P. & Kitchener, A.C. 1996. Second-generation rodenticides and Polecats *Mustela putorius* in Britain. *Environmental Pollution* 91: 279-282.

Shore, R.F., Afsar, A., Horne, J.A. & Wright, J. 2000. *Rodenticide and lead concentrations in Red Kites* Milvus milvus. Centre for Ecology and Hydrology, Huntingdon.

Shrubb, M. 2003. *Birds, Scythes and Combines: A history of birds and agricultural change.* Cambridge University Press, Cambridge.

Simmons, R.E., Avery, D.M. & Avery, G. 1991. Biases in diets determined from pellets and remains: correction factors for a mammal and bird-eating raptor. *Journal of Raptor Research* 25: 63-67.

Snell, N., Dixon, W., Freeman, A., McQuaid, M. & Stevens, P. 2002. Nesting behaviour of the Red Kite in the Chilterns. *British Wildlife* 13: 177-183.

Snow, D.W. & Perrins, C.M. 1998. *The Birds of the Western Palearctic: Concise Edition Vol. 1.* Oxford University Press, Oxford.

Snyder, N. & Snyder, H. 2000. *The California Condor: A Saga of Natural History and Conservation.* Academic Press, London.

SOVON. 1987. *Atlas van de Nederlandse Vogels.* SOVON, Arnhem [In Dutch with English summary].

SOVON. 2002. *Atlas van de Nederlandse Broedvogels, 1998-2000.* SOVON Vogelanderzoek Nederland, Leiden.

Squires, A. & Jeeves, M. 1994. *Leicestershire and Rutland Woodlands: Past and present.* Kairos Press, Newton Linford.

Stott, M., Callion, J., Kinley, I., Raven, C. & Roberts, J. (eds.) 2002. *The Breeding Birds of Cumbria: A tetrad atlas 1997-2001.* Cumbria Bird Club.

Stubbe, M. 1982. Brutdichte und alterstruktur einer Rotmilan-Population *Milvus milvus* – im nördlichen Harzvorland der DDR im vergleich zum Mäusebussard *Buteo buteo. Arch. Naturschutz Landscharftsforschung* 22: 205-214.

Svensson, L., Grant, P.J., Mullarney, K. & Zetterström, D. 1999. *Collins Bird Guide.* HarperCollins, London.

Taylor, M., Seago, M., Allard, P. & Dorling, D. 1999. *The Birds of Norfolk.* Pica Press, Robertsbridge.

Terrasse, M., Sarrazin, F., Choisy, J-P., Clémente, C., Henriquet, S., Lécuyer, P., Pinna, J-L. & Tessier, C. 2004. A success story: The reintroduction of Eurasian Griffon *Gyps fulvus* and Black *Aegypius monachus* Vultures to France. In: Chancellor, R.D. & Meyburg, B.-U. (eds.) *Raptors Worldwide, Proceedings of the VI World Conference on Birds of Prey and Owls*, 127-145. World Working Group on Birds of Prey and Owls/Birdlife Hungary, Budapest.

Thiollay, J.M. & Bretagnolle, V. 2004. *Rapaces Nicheurs de France, Distribution, Effectifs et Conservacion.* Delachaux & Niestlé, Paris.

Thiollay, J.M. & Terrasse, J.F. (eds.) 1984. *Estimation des effectifs de rapaces nicheurs diurnes et non rupestres en France.* Fonds d'Intervention pours les Rapaces, La Garenne-Colombes.

Thiollay, J.M., Bretagnolle, V. & Sériot, J. [in press] *Atlas des Rapaces Nicheurs de France, 2000-2003.*

Ticehurst, N.F. 1934. Rewards for vermin-killing paid by the churchwardens of Tenterden 1626-1712. *Hastings and East Sussex Naturalist* 5: 69-82.

Tjernberg, M. 1983. Habitat and nest site features of Golden Eagles *Aquila chrysaetos* in Sweden. *Swedish Wildlife Research* 12: 131-163.

Toms, M.P. & Clark, J.A. 1998. Bird ringing in Britain and Ireland in 1996. *Ringing & Migration* 19: 95-167.

Tubbs, C.R. 1974. *The Buzzard.* David & Charles, Newton Abbot.

Tucker, G.M. & Heath, M.F. (eds.) 1994. *Birds in Europe: Their Conservation Status.* Birdlife International, Cambridge.

Turner, W. 1544. *Avium Praecipuarum, quarum apud Plinium et Aristotelem mention est, brevis & succincta historia.*

Ulfstrand, S. 1963. The Red Kite *Milvus milvus* wintering in Scania, southern Sweden. *Vår Fågelvärld* 22: 182-195.

Urcun, J-P. & Bried, J. 1998. The autumn migration of Red Kite *Milvus milvus* through the Pyrenees. In: Chancellor, R.D., Meyburg, B.-U. & Ferrero, J.J. (eds.) *Holarctic Birds of Prey: Proceedings of an International Conference*, 641-654. World Working Group on Birds of Prey and Owls/ADENEX, Calamonte, Spain.

Van den Berg, A.B. & Bosman, C.A.W. 1999. *Rare Birds of the Netherlands.* Pica Press, Mountfield.

Van Kleef, H. & Bustamante, J. 1999. First recorded polygynous mating in the Red Kite *Milvus milvus. Journal of Raptor Research* 33: 254-257.

Veiga, J.P. & Hiraldo, F. 1990. Food habits and the survival and growth of nestlings in two sympatric kites (*Milvus milvus* and *Milvus migrans*). *Holarctic Ecology* 13: 62-71.

Villafuerte, R., Viñuela, J. & Blanco, J.C. 1998. Extensive predator persecution caused by population crash in a game species: The case of Red Kites and Rabbits in Spain. *Biological Conservation* 84: 181-188.

Village, A. 1990. *The Kestrel.* Poyser, London.

Viñuela, J. 1992, 1993, 1994. *Status of the Red Kite in Spain – Red Kite Project Research Reports.* SEO/Birdlife, Madrid.

Viñuela, J. 1996. Situacion del Milano Real *Milvus milvus* en el Mediterraneo. In: Muntaner, J. & Mayol, J. (eds.) *Biology and Conservation of Mediterranean Raptors, 1994*, 90-100. SEO Monographía No. 4, Madrid. [In Spanish with English summary].

Viñuela, J. 1997. Road transects as a large-scale census method for raptors: The case of the Red Kite *Milvus milvus* in Spain. *Bird Study* 44: 155-165.

Viñuela, J. & Ferrer, M. 1997. Regulation of growth in Red Kites and Imperial Eagles. *Wilson Bulletin* 109: 92-101.

Viñuela, J. & Sunyer, C. 1992. Nest orientation and hatching success of Black Kites *Milvus migrans* in Spain. *Ibis* 134: 340-345.

Viñuela, J. & Villafuerte, R. 2003. Predators and Rabbits *Oryctolagus cuniculus* in Spain: A key conflict for European raptor conservation. In: Thompson, D.B.A., Redpath, S.M., Fielding, A.H., Marquiss, M. & Galbraith, C.A. (eds.) *Birds of Prey in a Changing Environment*, 511-526. Scottish Natural Heritage, Edinburgh.

Viñuela, J., Martí, R. & Ruiz, A. 1999. *El Milano Real en España*. SEO/Birdlife Monografía No. 6, Madrid. [In Spanish with English summary].

Walls, S.S. & Kenward, R.E. 1995. Movements of radio-tagged Common Buzzards *Buteo buteo* in their first year. *Ibis* 137: 177-182.

Walters Davies, P. & Davis, P.E. 1973. The ecology and conservation of the Red Kite in Wales. *British Birds* 66: 183-224, 241-269.

Ward, P. & Zahavi, A. 1973. The importance of certain assemblages of birds as 'information centres' for finding food. *Ibis* 115: 517-534.

Warren, R.B. 1989. Red Kite and Black Kite following mowing-machine. *British Birds* 82: 116.

Watson, J. 1997. *The Golden Eagle*. Poyser, London.

Weber, M. & Stubbe, M. 1995. Biometrische Untersuchungen zu Eischalenveränderungen bei Rotmilan *Milvus milvus*, Schwarzmilan *Milvus migrans* und Mäusebussard *Buteo buteo* nach 1950. In: Richarz, K., Meyburg, B.-U. & Hormann, M. (eds.) Rotmilan-Sonderheft, 133-139. *Vogel und Umwelt*, Bd. 8. [In German with English summary].

Wiebe, K.L., Korpimäki, E. & Wiehn, J. 1998. Hatching asynchrony in Eurasian Kestrels in relation to the abundance and predictability of cyclic prey. *Journal of Animal Ecology* 67: 908-917.

Wildman, L., O'Toole, L. & Summers, R.W. 1998. The diet and foraging behaviour of the Red Kite in Scotland. *Scottish Birds* 19: 134-140.

Wink, M. & Sauer-Gürth, H. 2004. Phylogenetic relationships in diurnal raptors based on nucleotide sequences of mitochondrial and nuclear marker genes. In: Chancellor, R.D. & Meyburg, B.-U. (eds.) *Raptors Worldwide, Proceedings of the VI World Conference on Birds of Prey and Owls*, 483-498. World Working Group on Birds of Prey and Owls/Birdlife Hungary, Budapest.

Wotton, S.R., Carter, I., Cross, A.V., Etheridge, B., Snell, N., Duffy, K., Thorpe, R. & Gregory, R.D. 2002. Breeding status of the Red Kite *Milvus milvus* in Britain in 2000. *Bird Study* 49: 278-286.

Yalden, D.W. & Morris, P.A. 1990. *The analysis of owl pellets.* Mammal Society occasional publication No. 13.

Yarrell, W. 1857. *History of British Birds (revised edition).* Van Voorst, London.

Zeitz, R., Daróczi, S., Sándor, D.A. & Domahidi, Z. 1999. Preliminary results of the Transsylvanian raptor census program - pilot project for long term conservation and management. Raptor Research Conference, Trebon, Czech Republic. *Buteo* 10: 21.

INDEX